THE I

It could be said that the celebrated actor Laurence Martineau had been responsible for Katy leaving her job at Metropolitan Television; at any rate, he had offered her a temporary job as his secretary. Hadn't she jumped out of the frying pan into the fire, though? For though he was not as disagreeable as her previous boss had been, he had a dark, brooding attraction that looked like being far more lethal . . .

THE DARK ONE

THE DARK ONE

BY

VANESSA JAMES

MILLS & BOON LIMITED
15–16 BROOK'S MEWS
LONDON W1A 1DR

All the characters in this book have no existence out-side the imagination of the Author, and have no rela-tion whatsoever to anyone bearing the same name or names. They are not even distantly inspired by any individual known or unknown to the Author, and all the incidents are pure invention.

The text of this publication or any part thereof may not be reproduced or transmitted in any form or by any means, electronic or mechanical, including photo-copying, recording, storage in an information retrieval system, or otherwise, without the written permission of the publisher.

This book is sold subject to the condition that it shall not, by way of trade or otherwise, be lent, resold, hired out or otherwise circulated without the prior consent of the publisher in any form of binding or cover other than that in which it is published and without a similar condition including this condition being imposed on the subsequent purchaser.

First published 1982
Australian copyright 1982
Philippine copyright 1982
This edition 1982

© Vanessa James 1982

ISBN 0 263 73904 X

Set in Monophoto Times 9 on 10 pt.
01–0982 – 58923

Made and printed in Great Britain by
Richard Clay (The Chaucer Press) Ltd,
Bungay, Suffolk

CHAPTER ONE

THE sunlight was already streaming into the room, but it wasn't that which woke her, but the smell of her flatmate's burning toast, mingled with the scent of expensive bath-oil which eddied under the bedroom door. Katy sighed, turned over, looked at the clock—it said eight a.m. and any moment the alarm would ring—and decided to give herself five more minutes. Just five minutes more, she thought lazily, still half asleep. She had plenty of time still to get washed and dressed and catch the tube over to the studios.

Idly she let her mind run over the day ahead. The best thing, she thought, about working as a researcher for a talk-show, or chat-show, as everyone but her boss, the odious Dick Hunt, called it, was that there was no set routine. Anything might happen that day; it would depend on who was to be the guest that night. She had had a few days off earlier that week—her first break since she had joined the company seven months before, so she had no idea at all who it would be. Someone important, that was certain, because today was Friday, the day they recorded the longer of Dick Hunt's twice-weekly shows, the one that went out at prime time on Saturday, the one Dick Hunt reserved for the 'really big fish' as he called them . . .

For the millionth time Katy silently blessed her luck in securing this job. Dick Hunt himself might be a very different person from his public image, but it was usually possible to stay out of his way, and so far she hadn't been on the receiving end of one of his famous bouts of ill temper. And apart from that—well, it was a wonderful job. All her friends were envious and the salary was so good; it paid for this flat; it had made her independent for the first time in her life . . .

'Katy!'

There was a crash of crockery from the kitchen, followed by an anguished shriek. Katy smiled to herself. Par for the course, she thought. Jane managed not only to burn toast, but also to break at least one plate or cup per day. She was always threatening to replace the whole lot with cardboard ones from Woolworth's.

'Coming!' she called, and threw back the sheets. She stretched and pulled on a cotton dressing gown and padded barefoot to the kitchen. Jane was standing in an attitude of dismay, her head swathed in a towel, the remains of the milk jug at her feet. An expression of guilt was etched on her face.

'Well,' she said finally, 'look at it this way. At least it got you up. You don't want to be late for the studios, do you?'

Katy grinned and helped her pick up the fragments.

'And what's more,' Jane went on, 'I'm going to be late again, because I washed my hair for a particular reason today. It's not dry yet, and it takes nearly an hour to get into the West End for this stupid job. I can't think why I ever took it in the first place. Why can't I get a wonderful romantic, glamorous job like you, Katy, having lunch with film stars and taking tea with statesmen . . .'

'A lot of people think that photography's glamorous! And I'm usually sitting in an office putting up with Dick Hunt's tantrums,' Katy said wryly. She knew she was wasting her words. Nothing she did or said could ever convince Jane that working for Metropolitan Television was not just a bed of roses. She stopped, for Jane had just clapped her hand melodramatically across her lips.

'Oh *damn*!' she exclaimed. 'Katy—I totally forgot! The studio rang late last night, there was some crisis on or something, and you were out, of course . . .'

Katy felt the familiar lift of excitement, tinged with exasperation. 'Who rang? Did they say what it was about?'

But Jane was dragging off the towel, and her wet head emerged from clouds of scented steam. She disappeared in the direction of the nearest mirror, and when she returned her face, still unmade-up, looked distinctly bad-tempered. She stood framed in the kitchen doorway, peering at Katy shortsightedly. Jane, without her contact lenses, without her elaborate, amazing make-up, always looked curiously vulnerable, as if she had not yet donned her skin.

'Well,' she said, 'that dye was a disaster. Look at this.'

Katy stared in horror. The hair, still wet, was indeed an extraordinary shade, slightly pink, like strawberries diluted with water. Jane, a photographer's assistant with ambitions to be a photographic model, never looked exactly conventional, though she had an off-beat prettiness. Now she resembled a tall angular clown.

'Go ahead,' she said defiantly. 'Laugh! I know it looks a sight. Of course, if I had chestnut hair halfway down my back like you, I wouldn't have to bother with all this. As it is . . .' She sighed, and slumped into a kitchen chair.

'Maybe it'll look O.K. when it's dry,' said Katy tentatively, no great conviction in her voice.

Jane gave her a withering glance.

'Maybe it will and probably it won't,' she said acidly. 'If it doesn't, I'll just have to stuff the whole lot under a hat and hope for the best. It doesn't matter, of course. Don't break your heart. It only just so happens that today's the day they've finally agreed to take some test pictures of me round at Freddie's studio.'

Katy grinned. She had no doubts that Jane would be able to effect some stunning transformation of the lank strawberry locks, or that the session at Freddie's studio would turn out to be a success. Jane would achieve her ambitions, she thought, she was that kind of person.

'Talking of studios,' she said carefully, because with Jane in this mood you had to tread gently, 'when the office rang last night, they didn't by any chance leave a message? No panic, of course, but it might *just* be important.'

Sarcasm was wasted on Jane, but she did have the grace, Katy noted, to look slightly guilty.

'Oh, *hell*!' she said simply. 'I am sorry, love. They did. It was Lindy. I said you were out, and she said would you be sure to call her back first thing this morning, and I meant to write a note and stick it on your pillow, so you'd find it when you got back from being wined and dined by the delightful Bob. And then this morning I put this stuff on my hair, and it looked so ghastly I totally forgot . . .' She looked at the clock on the kitchen table, which now said eight-thirty. 'Is it late to be calling in, now, do you think? Will they be furious?'

In spite of herself, Katy laughed. Jane was impossible! But her self-absorption was so total, and the wicked teasing way she mentioned Bob's name was so obvious, that Katy had to forgive her. If Jane could divert the conversation from the fact that she'd forgotten to give Katy an important message, to the subject of Bob (to whom, it pleased her to pretend, she considered Katy was practically engaged) then she would. But Katy was not to be drawn.

'I shouldn't think I'll be fired. But you know what they're like, and if there's a crisis I should have rung in earlier. Never mind, I'll do it now. Did Lindy say what it was all about?'

Jane shook her head, and shrugged. Seeing that she was forgiven, she had already lost interest. 'No, not exactly,' she said, reaching for an orange and absently peeling it. 'She sounded in a terrible flap, though. Said they'd got some big name for the show tonight, and there was a huge drama going on . . .'

'Thanks a bunch,' said Katy wryly, and the words were hardly out of her mouth before the telephone in the sitting room next door began to shrill.

'That'll be Lindy now, I expect,' said Jane, with maddening unconcern. Katy hurried through and grabbed the receiver, and—of course—Jane was right. Lindy's voice sounded breathless with anxiety. Lindy was the senior researcher on the Dick Hunt Show; she had years of experience, and yet she panicked easily. She was certainly panicked now, Katy thought.

'Katy!' she wailed. 'Why didn't you ring me earlier? I left a message last night, and I've been in here since seven-thirty this morning . . .'

'Sorry, Lindy,' Katy said quickly. 'The message got to me about five seconds before you rang.'

An audible groan came down the line, and a muttered swearword. Lindy *must* be in a state, Katy thought, because she rarely swore. She felt her own pulses quicken. Something must indeed be up. Whoever had Dick Hunt managed to get for the programme that was causing all this fuss? Normally the weekend guests were lined up days before, and it was unusual to have a last-minute flap like this unless the guests were being swapped around. And that would never happen unless Dick Hunt had managed to hook a *very* big fish indeed . . .

'Listen carefully, Katy, for goodness' sake!' Lindy's voice was breathless. 'Everything is in chaos here. I've got strict instructions from Dick as to exactly what you're to do . . .'

'What's happened?' Katy couldn't help interrupting. 'Who has Dick got? Do you want me to come over at once? Can you send a taxi?'

'No. Stay where you are. It's the most extraordinary thing. You're not going to believe this. Dick's going to do the whole show with only one guest. And you'll never guess who it is . . .'

'Mickey Mouse,' Katy interjected, trying to deflate her own rising nervousness as much as Lindy's.

'*Shut up*, Katy! It's a big secret. Stop making feeble jokes. They're not announcing it until later today, and you mustn't breathe a word to anybody. They've only just clinched the deal . . .' Her voice sank to a conspiratorial whisper. 'It's . . . Laurence Martineau.'

Even on the telephone Katy could sense the reverence in Lindy's voice, and she felt her head start to spin.

'*What?*' she said weakly. 'But that's impossible! He . . .'

'It's true. He's arriving by plane this morning.'

'Laurence Martineau?' Katy could hear her own voice take on a rising note of panic and disbelief. 'But he's never given an interview. Never. Not even to the papers, let alone on television. I don't believe it!'

'Katy, for goodness' sake, will you shut up? It's *true*, I'm telling you. I don't know how Dick clinched it, and I don't suppose I ever will, but he has, and he's in a flat panic. He's rushing round the building downing cups of black coffee and bawling everybody's head off. I've never seen him so nervous before, not even when it was Jimmy Carter. Now listen, you've got to do two things and do them quickly. Dick wants you to go round to the Press Association now, and Xerox everything they've got on Martineau immediately. Two copies, one for you, and one to be put in a car and sent round to the studios, he needs them by ten-thirty at the latest . . .'

'But why?' Katy's head was whirling. 'Why does he want me to do that—surely you've got all the cuttings up from the company's library already . . .' The TV company kept an extensive library of press cuttings, as good as, if not better than, most Fleet Street libraries; she had never been asked to do this before.

'Katy, stop *arguing*! We've been through our cuttings already. There's practically nothing—he doesn't do interviews, remember? There's just a whole lot of reviews, and gossip column stuff, and tons on the divorce, of course, and interviews with Camilla Drew, "My anguish with Laurence

Martineau", that sort of thing. Dick's not satisfied. He wants to make sure there's nothing we've missed, so you've got to check out the P.A. Library. Quickly.'

'O.K.,' Katy drew a deep breath. 'I'll get a cab—I can be there in half an hour. What am I supposed to do with the other copies – the ones I don't send round to you?'

'Read them in the car on the way to the airport.'

'The *airport*?'

Lindy managed a nervous laugh. 'Yes, the airport. Guess who's the lucky girl who's meeting his plane?'

'*What?*' Katy felt her stomach turn over with nervousness. '*I've* got to meet him?'

'Yes, dear. Dick's special instructions. You and no one else. It must be to do with your dark brown eyes and well known charm. Now, hurry. Have you got a pencil?'

'Yes.'

'Right, take this down. There will be two cars waiting for you at the Press Association at ten-fifteen. Give one set of Xeroxes to the first driver—he'll bring them here to the studios. Get in the second car and read the others on the way to Heathrow. You're to meet the Air France plane, flight number AF 264, that leaves Toulon at eleven a.m., gets into Heathrow, Terminal 2, at twelve-fifteen. The car will wait. You meet him off the plane, take him to the car, and come with him to the studios. Dick will be waiting, and there's a champagne lunch for him on the fifth floor. We're not invited. Got that?'

Katy was scribbling furiously, and realised her hand was shaking. 'Got it,' she said. 'But Lindy, why me? Why aren't you doing this?'

'God moves in mysterious ways,' Lindy's voice was dry. 'Ours is not to reason why. Maybe it's to do with the fact that I haven't got a twenty-one-inch waist, and legs like Cyd Charisse. Just an Oxford degree. Now, hurry!' Katy could hear that the other telephones on her desk were starting to shrill. 'Listen, I must go. It's the *Mail*—they must have got wind of the story. Hurry. Oh—and good luck!' Lindy rang off, and Katy stood by the telephone, her hands damp with sweat, her legs shaking.

Laurence Martineau; she remembered the first time she had seen him on the stage. Her father had taken her up to London to see his *Hamlet* at the Old Vic. It was the performance which had established his fame, before they began calling him the greatest classical actor of his generation, before he had gone to Hollywood, and the film companies had begun queueing up for his services.

Her mind flashed back to that night nine years earlier, and she could see and hear him as clearly as she had then. The tall, dark figure, with brooding eyes, the swift athleticism of his movements. And the voice, capable of a thousand inflections, infinite cadences, one moment harsh and threatening, the next infinitely gentle, the next reaching out to every woman in the audience with a startling sensuality.

Laurence Martineau. Renowned for his coldness, his un-approachability. The man who had once smashed a photo-grapher's camera when they tried to take pictures of him in the street. The man rumoured to have turned down the advances of innumerable film sirens, and the offer of a knight-hood, with similar brusqueness. Laurence Martineau.

She wished very much that it was Lindy, not her, who had to meet him at the airport.

Katy had never dressed so quickly in her life. Luckily, Jane—who had managed to convert her appearance into one of spec-tacular elegance—was already leaving. She rushed into the bathroom and washed with what seemed like record speed; she thanked heaven that she rarely bothered with make-up. It was early September, and still warm, so she dragged out a light linen suit that she had worn for her elder sister's wedding. It was beautifully cut, a dress with a full, soft skirt, and a loose jacket of a rich creamy colour that looked well against her lightly tanned skin, and the dark chestnut of her hair. Rummaging in a drawer, she found her favourite necklace, the one her father had given her the year before he died, of old rough coral strung with silver beads. She brushed her hair vigorously, and stood looking critically at herself in the glass.

She saw a tall, slender girl, with a riot of thick hair falling around her face and on to her shoulders. A narrow, delicate face, with high wide cheekbones and very dark eyes. The mouth was too full, the nose too freckled, she thought, but then she had never particularly liked the way she looked. You look too boyish, she thought resignedly, and for the millionth time. Your legs are too long, your hips too narrow, and your shoulders too broad. Still, she didn't think Laurence Martineau would care much, either way, so there was no point in wasting time. She'd better just concentrate on getting to the cuttings library as quickly as possible. If she kept him waiting or—worse—was late getting to the airport, she could just imagine the scenes at the studio later that day.

As quickly as she could, she raced down the stairs from the flat and out into the street. She was lucky: the sun was shining, the streets of Little Venice, where she lived, were bathed in light; the boats moored in the canal basin that gave the area its name bobbed gently on glinting water. Her spirits lifted; there was even an empty cab, waiting in the rank by the church.

She got to Fleet Street quickly, for the driver took a clever route through back streets, avoiding all the traffic. The P.A. cuttings Library was a long, dark smoky room, wedged with tall filing cabinets and tucked away on the upper floors of a huge marble-fronted building in Fleet Street. It was crammed with desks, and with men in shirt-sleeves who sat in the dim light cutting up newspapers, annotating and filing the stories. Katy was used to such libraries now, but it never ceased to amaze her how efficient they were. Anyone featured in the news would have a file on them: stars, criminals, politicians; everything that had ever been printed about them would be there. How horrible, she often thought, never to be able to escape your past, but to have it all there on record, so that everything could always be raked up, repeated, re-examined, even gossip twenty years old.

Lindy had obviously telephoned ahead of her, because the librarian had Laurence Martineau's file waiting on an empty desk. It looked bulky, and Katy looked at her watch nervously: nine-fifteen. She had just an hour to go through it, Xerox anything that looked important, and get down to the car. Her heart sinking, she seated herself at the desk. She opened the little green filing case in which the cuttings were collected, and felt her heart lurch as they fanned out in front of her. There, on the top of the pile, was a photograph; there was the face that was already burned in her brain. The dark, alert gaze, the slightly twisted, deeply sensual mouth, those perfectly etched features that somehow always communicated a hurt, and underlying sadness, even when he smiled. Trying to steady herself, she began to arrange the cuttings in piles. This was just part of her job, she told herself. Nothing out of the ordinary. Why was she so nervous?

The hour passed very quickly, and Katy felt her panic mounting. The cuttings went back twenty years. Martineau was thirty-eight now; he had first gone on the stage when he was eighteen. Every performance he had given, every bit of gossip, everything that had been written or said about him since then was there in the dusty file. There wasn't enough time, she realised hopelessly. She'd just have to get most of them copied, and try and skim quickly through her set in the car on the way to the airport. After all, she really only needed to find out what he was doing at the moment. Just enough to fill her in so she could make conversation on the way back to the studios after she'd met his plane. As for Dick Hunt—well, he'd just have to cope, she thought rebelliously.

This whole exercise seemed pointless anyway. She was sure that most of this stuff would be in the cuttings at Metropolitan's library. Dick was only double checking . . . But just the thought of making conversation to Laurence Martineau made her heart turn over with nervousness. It would take the best part of an hour to get from Heathrow to Metropolitan, and the thought of sitting next to that tall, brooding man so famous for his hatred of journalists, terrified her. On the other hand, she thought wryly, she could hardly sit there in total silence. That would be even worse.

At ten-fifteen she hurried downstairs. Outside the P.A. building, there were two cars drawn up with grand disdain for the double yellow lines that ran right along the street. The first was the normal Metropolitan vehicle, one of the fleet of Fords that were kept at the programme's disposal. The second was a large gleaming black Daimler, with a uniformed chauffeur. If anything was calculated to make Katy more nervous, it was that. A Daimler! The programme was really putting out the red carpet.

She handed the envelope of cuttings for Dick Hunt to the driver of the Ford, Joe, whom she knew well. He cocked his thumb at the Daimler drawn up behind him.

'Ritzy treatment, eh, Katy? Anyway, good luck, love. I hear Martineau's a right s.o.b. Even worse than . . .' And he named another celebrated guest who had often appeared on Hunt's show, and was famous throughout the studios for ill-temper and rudeness. When he saw Katy's face fall, he grinned cheerily.

'Chin up, love. Don't let them grind you down. Remember, they've sent you because you're the charmer!'

He accelerated off, and Katy climbed into the Daimler, settling back in the deep leather seats. The driver merely nodded at her curtly, did an illegal U-turn, and revved away, shooting the first red lights they came to.

Katy sat there trying not to feel annoyed. That was the second person who had implied she had been chosen to meet Laurence Martineau because of her supposed charms, she thought crossly. It made her feel stupid, like a piece of bait, the tender morsel who was being used to soften Martineau up. She could almost hear Dick Hunt giving the instructions: 'Send Katy to the airport. She looks O.K. If anyone can butter Martineau up, she can . . .'

Some chance! she thought, opening the cuttings file again, and balancing it on her knees as the driver sped the car north. Quite apart from the fact that she had no intention of being used that way, Laurence Martineau was the last man on earth to fall for it.

Everything in the file in front of her bore that out. His guard over his own privacy was obviously ferocious, and he never let it drop. The file was full of reviews, but she noted, not one interview, just as she had remembered. There were the photographs of his *Hamlet*, and it was just as she remembered it from all those years ago. Except that his wife-to-be, Camilla Drew, was the Ophelia. How odd! She had completely forgotten that. Searching her memory, even looking at the picture, she could remember nothing of Camilla Drew's performance at all. And even when he swept all the awards for that performance, and signed his first Hollywood contract, not one interview. Just quotes from short, terse speeches of thanks at award ceremonies. And then the divorce.

There were pages about that all right. There was plenty there that would delight Dick Hunt, she thought grimly, as she scanned the columns. Camilla Drew obviously didn't share her husband's distaste for talking to the press—quite the opposite! Katy stared in dislike at the endless pictures. Camilla

Drew in nightclubs. Camilla Drew at premières. The 'confidential' interviews . . . '"No woman could live with this man," a tearful Camilla Drew told me yesterday at Claridges . . . Grounds for divorce will be mental cruelty, I hear, though London is also buzzing with tales of physical violence, and when we met Camilla had one arm discreetly bandaged . . .'

In all this, nothing from Martineau himself. Katy riffled through the pages; no, nothing. No answer to his wife's allegations. He hadn't even attended the divorce hearing. Camilla had, wearing a different outfit for each of the three days it lasted, Katy noted scornfully, as she peered at the photographs. One in particular caught her attention; Camilla Drew was outside the High Court. She was swathed in furs, the familiar icily beautiful blonde features gazing haughtily at the camera. She was leaning on the arm of a man slightly obscured in the picture, and unidentified.

Katy held it up to the light. Surely it was Dick Hunt? It was difficult to tell, because the picture was blurred, and the movement of the Daimler made scrutiny difficult. Also, it dated from some five years back, before Dick made his name, long before Katy had ever known him. Now his hair was receding badly, and this man certainly had more hair than the Dick Hunt she knew now. But the pudgy pallid features, the pugilist's nose and narrow tight mouth . . . surely it was the same? But she couldn't be sure, and anyway, she thought, pushing the cutting back into the file, there was no reason why it shouldn't be Dick Hunt. Before he had become famous as an investigative interviewer, he had been a minor television reporter. Though even then (or so Lindy said), he had avidly courted the famous. It would have been just his drop, Katy thought with dislike, to escort a woman like Camilla Drew to a messy divorce hearing. She looked rich and mean; she and Dick ought to suit each other very well, Katy thought, and then forgot about it.

The car was slowing down, and looking out of the window, she realised that they were turning off towards the airport. Hastily she stowed the press cuttings away in her bag, and reached for her pocket mirror. Her eyes, almost black, fringed with thick lashes and wide with anxiety, looked back at her from a pale face. She smoothed some powder on her nose, and attempted to brighten her lips with a deep coral lipstick,

but the movement of the car and her shaking hand didn't
improve matters, and she gave up the attempt. To hell with it,
she thought. She didn't care what she looked like, or what Mr
Laurence Martineau thought of her. She'd be polite, impersonal and calm, and just concentrate on getting him back
to the studios on time.

The chauffeur pulled into the space reserved for VIP cars at
Terminal 2 and Katy raced inside. Her eyes scanned the building for the arrivals board. It was eleven-fifteen. Calm down,
she told herself, you've got plenty of time; just get to the right
gate, sit there till he comes, and try not to make an idiot of
yourself. AF264 was due to disembark from Gate 7, and
Katy raced up the stairs two at a time, and along the concourse, until she had Gate 7 right opposite her. That part of
the terminal was deserted. A few businessmen were hiring cars
at the Hertz desk; some tourists were changing currency at the
Bureau de Change. No one else seemed to be waiting for Flight
264, and Katy found an empty bench, tucked away behind a
partition.

She sat down, feeling calmer. The flight was on time, it
seemed, everything was going smoothly. Relax, relax, she said
to herself, and the wild tattoo her pulse had been beating (the
run up the staircase) gradually slowed.

The mystery of it all, she thought, as she sat there quietly,
was that Laurence Martineau should be doing this interview
at all. Why on earth should someone who had always refused
to talk to the press suddenly agree to appear on television,
and with Dick Hunt, of all people? Maybe he didn't realise
what he was in for, she thought bitterly; he lived abroad now,
the cuttings said, and was rarely in England. Maybe he'd never
seen Dick Hunt's show ... But no, that was impossible, she
thought. Even if he'd never seen it, he must know the kind of
revelations that had made the show famous, and Dick Hunt
rich—the revelations that made headlines all round the world.
The amazing thing, she thought, was that *anyone* ever agreed
to appear with Dick Hunt, but they did. And then the routine
would go into action. The soft-touch introductions, the copi-
ous 'hospitality'—the studio's word for too many free drinks.
And the celebrities to be interviewed gradually relaxing,
dropping their guard ... It was all carefully controlled, of
course, Dick Hunt saw to that. No one was allowed to get

drunk, that would blow the programme. They were just fed
enough alcohol and enough flattery to soften them up, and
then, in studio, Dick Hunt would go into his famous routine.
The easy questions to begin with, lulling them further. And
then suddenly, when he sensed the moment had come for the
kill, the sudden shaft of a question that went straight to the
jugular. It made superb television, as Dick was so fond of
reminding his staff. 'This isn't one of those soft chat-shows,'
he had said to Katy, when he first interviewed her for her job.
'I *talk*. I investigate. If they've got something to hide, I find
it . . .'

And so he did, and got more famous and more rich in the
process. He didn't have to worry about the resignations, the
gossip, the broken marriages, the scandals, that invariably
followed one of his shows. And perhaps he was right, Katy
thought defensively. For after all, the programme had uncovered some affairs that deserved exposing, that was why she
stayed . . . Bob had thought she was mad to take the job in
the first place, of course. But the thought of Bob made her
uncomfortable and she pushed it away from her. After all,
what did Bob know about it? Bob had known her since she
was a child; to him she was the little girl next door. He didn't
realise she was grown up now, and able to make her own
decisions.

Katy sighed, and looked at her watch. Ten minutes to go.
Although she was sitting calmly, her palms felt damp, and she
pressed them against her skirt. She stared at the gate opposite
her, behind which she could glimpse shadowy shapes. Had the
flight arrived early? Could that be Laurence Martineau, clear-
ing Customs? But the doors swung back, and only a few airline
staff came through, so she relaxed again. What line would
Dick Hunt have on his star guest? she wondered. Judging from
the cuttings she'd read, it was just the kind of interview he
relished. After all, he could spot someone's weak spots at a
hundred yards, and Laurence Martineau's were obvious. She
could almost hear Dick Hunt's voice: 'Well now, Mr
Martineau, we know that you received a million dollars for
your last film, but the critics didn't like it thàt much. Is it
money that's keeping you out of the theatre?'

Suddenly there was a flurry of activity at Gate 7; the doors
were flung back and the first bunch of passengers came

through. Katy leapt to her feet, her eyes scanning their faces, searching for that tall dark figure she remembered so well . . . There were a couple of teenagers with rucksacks. Some middle-aged women laden with bags. A businessman, short and be-spectacled, carrying a plastic briefcase. Katy tensed. Where was he? Oh God, she prayed silently, don't let anything go wrong. Five minutes passed. Four more passengers filtered out—a family, with small children. Then nothing. She waited another ten minutes. It was nearly twelve-forty-five, she realised. Surely he should be through Customs and Immigration now? Perhaps he had missed the flight, she thought, and then suddenly, *perhaps he's not coming*. To her own surprise, that thought slightly lifted her spirits. She would be quite glad, Katy realised, if Laurence Martineau *didn't* give Dick Hunt the interview coup of a lifetime.

Finally she saw the Air France flight crew come through the gate, and she stepped quickly across to intercept them.

'Excuse me,' she spoke to the stewardess, but the steward, who was tall and fair, stopped and turned. He gave her an odd Gallic half-bow, and the French stewardess glared at her.

'I can be of assistance, *mademoiselle?*'

Blushing under his intent gaze, Katy explained.

'But this is no problem . . .' He brought out a clipboard. 'I have the passenger list here. Martineau, you say?' He ran his finger down the list with maddening slowness. 'No, I am sorry, *mademoiselle*,' he said finally. 'There was no Monsieur Martineau on this flight. We were less than half full. And had Monsieur Martineau been aboard, I should certainly have known it.'

At this point the stewardess, who was watching suspiciously, suddenly seemed to understand what was being discussed; she began jabbering to the steward in rapid French. He nodded, and then turned back to Katy.

'Ah yes, it is so, *mademoiselle*. It is not on my list. Monsieur Martineau *was* booked. His flight was cancelled by telephone this morning.'

'Thank you.' Katy started to turn away, suddenly over-whelmed with a feeling of relief. He wasn't coming! Still, she had better make sure . . .

'There is no later flight he could be on today?'

The steward shook his head. 'I regret, no, *mademoiselle*,' he said. 'There is only one flight from Toulon each day. The next is at the same time tomorrow morning.'

He gave her another half-bow, and a glance of such naked admiration that the French stewardess practically frogmarched him away. Katy almost laughed aloud. Her heart suddenly felt light. Hooray! Laurence Martineau had had the good taste not to come after all, he had changed his mind, she could relax. Now she could go back to the studios and have the pleasure of watching Dick Hunt try to reconstruct his evening's programme. She would go down to the airport canteen and get a well-earned cup of coffee, she thought. Let the Daimler wait. And she had better ring Lindy and let her know the news . . .

She had gone the length of the concourse, and was just crossing towards the telephones, when she heard the announcement.

'Would Miss Katharine Sutcliffe of Metropolitan Television please come to the VIP arrivals lounge immediately. Would Miss Katharine Sutcliffe . . .'

She froze in her tracks. That could only mean one thing. He was in the airport after all, and somehow she had missed him . . . Her mind whirled. But that was impossible. He hadn't been on the flight, he'd cancelled his ticket . . . Desperately she scanned the direction boards, and raced up the stairs to the plain teak doors marked simply *VIP Arrivals*. There was no time to compose herself.

A British Airways official stopped her at the door. She flashed her TV staff card at him, and he let her through. Katy paused just inside the door, gazing anxiously around her, dimly aware that she must look hot and dishevelled—not the cool, calm controlled creature she had planned to be at all.

The lounge was almost deserted, and she saw him immediately, in the same moment that he saw her. He stood up, and Katy stared, unable to move for a moment.

CHAPTER· TWO

HER first thought was how tall he looked, and how command-
ing. He was wearing an immaculately cut dark suit, a white
shirt, and a black silk tie. His cuffs showed exactly the correct
length below his jacket sleeves, and there was a discreet dull
gleam of gold cufflinks. His suit was uncreased, he carried no luggage. He simply stood there, the dark thick hair falling across
his brow over the deep-set coal-black eyes. The wide, sensual
mouth was unsmiling. At twenty-five yards, you could feel the
famous power and magnetism emanating from him, effortlessly.
He simply looked at her, and waited for her to cross to him.

Katy hurried across the thick red carpet, trembling with
nervousness. 'Mr Martineau?'

She had come to a halt about a yard from him, and she
could feel the stern eyes blazing with anger.

'You're late,' he said curtly, cutting right across her apolo-
gies. She swallowed quickly.

'I'm terribly sorry, Mr Martineau. I was told to meet the
flight from Toulon that arrived at twelve-fifteen . . . I've been
waiting at the arrivals gate . . .'

Her voice trailed away, and he looked at her coldly.

'I changed my plans,' he said. 'I flew from Paris. My secretary informed your office earlier this morning. I'm surprised
they didn't tell you.'

There was a clear implication, Katy thought, that she was
not telling the truth, that she was inventing excuses. She felt
her own anger rising quickly.

'I was not at the studios this morning, Mr Martineau,' she
said crisply. 'I expect the studio tried to contact me, and
couldn't reach me.'

'How efficient of them,' he said, in the famous, slightly sarcastic rasping voice. Her anger deepened, and she took a deep
breath; she must *not* allow this man to upset her.

'I'm extremely sorry that you've had to wait, Mr
Martineau.' She attempted a cool, professional smile. It didn't

go down very well. He consulted his watch with elaborate slowness.

'A mere hour,' he said. 'Don't let it worry you.'

So—he had been here at eleven-forty-five. Then why hadn't he had the sense to get them to make a Tannoy announcement earlier? she thought irritably. 'I do apologise,' she said again, with an effort, trying to stop her eyes blazing their annoyance. 'Did you telephone the studio?'

'No, I didn't,' he said mockingly. 'I thought I would sit here in this extremely comfortable lounge, and observe the passers-by, and see just how long it took your organisation to sort itself out.'

The insult was now so gratuitous that she glared at him. 'Well, they have sorted things out to the extent that a car is waiting, Mr Martineau. Would you like to come downstairs?'

'But of course.'

He moved ahead of her, and opened the doors with the same mocking elaborateness with which he had consulted his watch. Katy felt furious. She hated him. Everything they've ever written about you is quite right, she thought, rude, cold, sarcastic, impossible man! Well, he wasn't going to get the better of her. She marched slightly ahead of him, head held high. As they passed through the airport, she saw all heads turn, a flashbulb popped, and Laurence Martineau walked through it all as cool as a cucumber, perfectly indifferent to the stir he knew he was causing. The car, she saw with huge relief, was waiting, engine running. The chauffeur saw them coming, leapt out, and was round to open the rear door, hat doffed, with impeccable timing.

Laurence Martineau ignored him. To her surprise, he took Katy's arm in a firm grip just above the elbow, and helped her first into the car. Then he seated himself beside her, and turned his face away towards the window. Free from his gaze, she looked at him with frank curiosity.

It was an extraordinarily powerful and beautiful face, not a modern face at all, she thought. There was nothing modish or fashionable about it. It was, quite simply, perfectly formed, but with an underlying savagery that came from the jut of the chin, the deep lines from nose to mouth, the fierceness of those dark, deep-set eyes. It was a man's face. She couldn't imagine it as a boy's.

He gazed moodily out of the window, ignoring her. His long, finely formed hands rested in his lap, perfectly relaxed. He wore no wedding ring, Katy noticed (not that she would have expected him to); just a gold signet ring with a crest on the little finger of his left hand. She was staring down at that when suddenly she realised that he had turned and was looking intently at her.

She was intensely aware of the proximity of that hard lean body on the seat next to her, and she felt the blood rising in her cheeks, and saw that he noted it.

For the first time, he smiled, a long slow mocking smile that lifted the sensual curve of his lips, and seemed to light up the whole face.

'You *are* Katharine Sutcliffe, I suppose?' he said finally. 'I was told she would be meeting me.'

'Yes, I am,' she said stiffly.

He gave her a long, hard stare, and Katy lowered her eyes instinctively to protect them from that fierce, enquiring gaze.

'Well, Katharine Sutcliffe,' he said, 'I would imagine, wouldn't you, that you've been sent here to charm and relax me on the way to the studio? I'm waiting for you to begin.'

That did it. Nervousness and tension made her temper finally snap—and she had a quick temper at the best of times anyway.

'I'm here merely to meet you, Mr Martineau,' she flashed at him. 'I simply have to ensure that you reach the studios with the minimum amount of fuss. Whether you're relaxed or not is up to you. And as for whether you're charmed—I can assure you I'm perfectly indifferent. I wouldn't expect you to be any more charmed by me than I am by you!'

There was silence. Katy knew her colour was up, and her hands felt slightly damp. Laurence Martineau looked at her coolly for a moment or two, giving her plenty of time to consider how she had probably just managed to lose her job. Then, to her complete surprise, he began to laugh. The laughter lit up his face and softened it.

'Well, well, well,' he said. 'What a little spitfire! So I don't charm you, Miss Sutcliffe? You have no idea what a relief that is to me. If you only knew how tired one could become of constant, senseless adulation.'

'It's a problem I've never had to contend with,' Katy said sharply. He looked at her appraisingly; his cool gaze travelled up from her legs, over her body, and rested with her face.

'Really?' he said drily. 'You *do* surprise me.'

She was really angry now, the more so because she knew he was playing on it. 'And I don't particularly like compliments, Mr Martineau,' she said hotly, 'especially sarcastic ones.'

His eyebrows arched ironically, but he ignored the remark. 'How long have you been doing your present job, Miss Sutcliffe?'

'Seven months,' she replied unwillingly.

He nodded superciliously. 'I thought it couldn't be very long. And before that?'

'I was at home. And before that——' she forestalled his question, 'I was at school. So, no, I'm not very experienced, Mr Martineau. But I'm learning every day.'

'Don't learn too much,' he said, 'and don't learn too quickly. I find you rather refreshing just as you are.'

This time the compliment—if it was one—sounded more sincere. Katy hesitated, feeling rather stupid and gauche.

'I'm sorry,' she said finally, 'I was rude, and I had no business to be.'

'But you did,' he said. 'I was rude to you. Perhaps we should call it quits?' To her surprise, he held out a long, slender hand, and solemnly took hers. His touch reverberated through her body, and Katy felt quite weak. She turned away, so that those penetrating, observant eyes should not see the expression on her face.

'Now,' he said, 'you must stop diverting me, and let me concentrate. I rather imagine that Dick Hunt is going to grill me this evening, so I'd better be prepared. I'm not exactly experienced at giving interviews, especially not to such a fearless campaigner for the truth. I wonder what it will be—my lamentable failure as a husband, or my refusal to return to the stage ...' Katy stared at him, astonished that his thinking should so echo her own, and should be so accurate. But she said nothing. He smiled gently, a little sadly, and turned away to the window once more. They spent the rest of the journey in silence.

Katy wrestled with her thoughts, trying to work out why it

was that this man had such a perturbing effect on her, and trying to calm herself down. She managed this to a degree, and by the time they reached the studios she felt much more in control.

They got out at the reception area, and Katy saw the receptionist nod to her and reach for the phone as she ushered Laurence Martineau to the lifts: the call would be to Dick Hunt to announce their arrival.

The lifts were old-fashioned, and slow. Laurence Martineau and Katy stood in awkward silence as they mounted to the fifth floor, until suddenly he turned to her and looked her in the eyes.

'Wish me luck,' he said. 'I think I may need it.'

It was a direct appeal, and Katy knew instantly that he meant it. What an ordeal it must be for him, she thought quickly, a man who had never given an interview to have to face Dick Hunt for an hour and a half in front of fifteen million television viewers. The light above the doors flashed the number '4', and she turned to him, touching his sleeve impulsively.

'I do wish you good luck,' she said. 'Remember he always asks the soft questions first—it's to put you off your guard . . .'

The lift doors opened, and there stood Dick Hunt, surrounded by the staff he liked to call his minions. His hand was already extended in welcome, and a wide insincere smile was pasted across his pallid features.

'Laurence Martineau!' he said dramatically, clasping him by the arm and drawing him into the corridor. 'Larry!—I may call you that?' The question was irrelevant, because he did not even pause for a reply. 'Well now, this *is* an honour. Excitement? I've never known anything like it! Now come along with me. Hope the flight wasn't too dreadful, hope we met you all right . . .' He ignored Katy completely, and she moved away, to go back to her office. Laurence Martineau forestalled her.

'Miss Sutcliffe,' the powerful voice stopped her in her tracks, and cut through Dick Hunt's waffle. She turned, and found herself looking once more into those dark, troubled eyes.

'I expect I shall see you later on,' he said simply. 'Meanwhile, thank you.' Katy saw Dick Hunt leer suggestively at a couple of his assistants, as if to say, 'I told you so. I knew Katy would soften him up O.K.'

'Not at all,' she said, as coolly and formally as she could. 'It was a pleasure, Mr Martineau.'

Laurence Martineau's eyebrows arched once more, and an ironic smile passed fleetingly across his face. Then he turned, Dick Hunt put a pudgy arm around his shoulders and drew him away down the corridor.

'Now, Larry,' he said, 'we thought a bit of lunch might help, something simple, a drop of champagne maybe ... must remember we're celebrating. I know it's nothing to you, but it's a red letter day for us, I can tell you ...'

They passed down the corridor, and Katy went back to her office, and sat down at her desk, feeling suddenly exhausted, and depressed. There would be nothing more for her to do now, except watch the programme. She hoped fiercely that Laurence Martineau would be able to deal with Dick, and she realised to her surprise that she had liked him. Rude, supercilious, he might be, but there was an honesty there, and something more, some deep sadness which she sensed but could not explain. She sighed and went to make herself some coffee. What she had said to him in the lift was, strictly speaking, unethical, she thought, but she was glad she had said it. Now there was nothing more she could do except sit at the side of the studio audience and watch the show. She had other routine work to get on with, but she couldn't settle to it. Her mind remained going over the events of the morning, and when Lindy came in with sandwiches, to announce that they were all up in the private dining room, Katy was snappish with her, and had to pretend she had a headache.

She worked in the office all afternoon, trying to concentrate. But the atmosphere of excitement penetrated even that room—people from the programme were constantly coming in and out, and the tension was building as the evening approached. They would begin taping the show at seven-thirty, in one of the large studios downstairs; there would be the usual studio audience of about a hundred and fifty people, and it was customary for all Dick Hunt's assistants and researchers to be there. By nine the show would be over, and then Dick Hunt usually took his guests out to dinner. Few of them refused, even the ones he had most savaged. Often they seemed slightly dazed by the whole experience, as if they didn't realise the damage they might have done themselves on the show. That realisation dawned later, when the show was transmitted over the weekend. Katy was wondering if Laurence Martineau would have dinner with Hunt, and was hoping that he might have the good taste to refuse, when at teatime Lindy came in again, looking flustered, and rang up Angelo's, the expensive Italian restaurant in Soho where Hunt liked to take his guests. She booked a table for six people at ten o'clock, and then rang off.

'Whew!' she exclaimed, dropping into a chair. 'I'm worn out. I've never known Dick in such a state.'

'So he's having dinner with him, then?' Katy said flatly.

'Of course.' Lindy stared at her. 'Did you think he wouldn't? No, apparently he's not going back to France for a couple of days, and he said he'd be delighted to have dinner. He's taking someone, and Dick's laid on some other guests, I think—don't know who.'

Katy felt oddly disappointed, but shrugged the feeling off; after all, it was nothing to do with her.

'Were the cuttings I found much help?' she asked; she still felt curious to know what line Hunt was going to take.

'I don't think so. Dick said there was nothing much we hadn't got already. I think he was just double-checking—if you ask me, he's got some line on Martineau—something he's found out. Anyway, he's playing his cards very close to his chest. At the moment it's the sweetness and light routine. We'll see what happens this evening.'

Lindy went down to the cafeteria to get something to eat, and Katy stayed behind in the office. She couldn't shake off the feeling of depression and anticlimax that hung over her.

Glancing across at Lindy's desk, she saw the file of Laurence Martineau press cuttings that had been sent off by car that morning. She got up and wandered around the office in a desultory way for a while, made herself some coffee, smoked a cigarette—which she rarely did. Finally she sat down with the coffee and flipped idly through Dick Hunt's copies of the cuttings; sometimes he marked those he was particularly interested in with red pencil, and one could get a vague idea of his line of questioning. But none of these was marked; they were all in the correct order, and appeared hardly to have been read. All the gossip, and the account of the Martineau divorce, lay in front of her again, and she was just about to bundle them all up and put them away when she noticed something odd. The cutting with the photograph showing Camilla Drew and the man who had resembled Dick Hunt was missing.

Katy stared at the file. How strange! She went to her bag, and checked her own copies, and then went back to Dick Hunt's. There was no question about it. She checked right through the pile. That cutting was missing; someone must have removed it. She wondered why. She looked again at the copy she had, holding the faded picture up to the light. But still she couldn't be sure; it could have been Dick Hunt, but it was impossible to be definite.

She looked at her watch—it was nearly six-thirty. She was just deciding that maybe she would go down to the canteen, and join Lindy, and have something to eat before the programme, when the door opened and Dick Hunt came in. He looked surprised to see her, and for some odd reason which Katy couldn't explain, she put the photograph she had been holding away in the file. She did it quickly, and Hunt seemed not to notice. He looked testy and on edge, and glared around the room.

'Where the hell is everybody?' he demanded. 'This is a television programme, not a pier-end concert.'

'Lindy's just gone down to the canteen,' Katy said. 'I was about to join her.'

'Lord, am I the only person around here who does any work?'

'I think she was tired,' she said quickly, 'she was in at seven-thirty this morning.'

'So?' He glowered at her, and for the umpteenth time, Katy thought what an unpleasant man he was. 'If you two don't like the hours you work, you can push off. There'd be a queue twice round the building if I advertised your jobs tomorrow.'

'I'm sure there would,' she said sweetly, and this seemed to mollify him slightly. The glower was replaced by an equally unpleasant leer, and he crossed the room and put an arm caressingly around her shoulders.

'You did a good job this morning, sweetie. Martineau seems

to have taken to you. What did you do to the guy? Was it your conversation or your legs that got to him?'

Katy felt physically sick, and managed to slide away from his touch.

'I think I'll go and get something to eat now, Dick, if that's O.K.'

He smiled, showing off the array of fine capped teeth.

'Little Miss Iceberg,' he said. 'What's wrong, Katy, aren't I famous enough for you? When are you going to have that dinner with me you promised?'

Katy had in fact never agreed to have dinner with him, let alone promised, as he very well knew. But it was true that from time to time he had asked her out. She disliked him too much to accept so much as a cup of canteen coffee from him, and she knew from Lindy about the little dinners with past researchers, and what they led to.

'I'm very busy, Dick,' she muttered, and made for the door.

'I can wait, sweetie. Just don't make me wait too long. I might get impatient . . .' He leered again, and blew her a wet kiss. 'Mind you watch the show tonight, there's bound to be some fireworks.'

'I wouldn't dream of missing it,' she said coldly, and shut the door quickly.

She ate a sandwich in the canteen, and tried not to listen to the make-up girls, who were twittering about Laurence Martineau, and how handsome he was.

'Oh, he was ever so nice,' said one. 'He autographed his picture for my son, and he was really charming. What a gentleman! Wouldn't hardly put any make-up on either—not that he needs it with that lovely tan. Not like a certain person I could mention.'

She and her friend giggled. They meant Dick Hunt, of course. He never appeared in the studios for a show until some poor girl had spent a good half hour working on him, shading out the bags under the eyes, washing and blow-drying his hair, and smoothing a special bronzer into his skin to disguise the pallor which showed up so badly under the studio lights.

Katy felt terribly nervous, and by the time she was due to go down to the studio to join the audience, she felt quite sick. She knew quite well that she had never felt like that before, and the realisation made her cross. Another victim of the famous Martineau charisma, she thought irritably. The studio was very hot, and the hundreds of lights glared down at the small set, furnished like an expensive modern room, where Hunt did his interviews. Cables and camera fitments snaked all over the floor, and there was the usual atmosphere of chaos and confusion, with dozens of cameramen and sound technicians. It would all resolve itself into order, as if by magic, as the count-down to the taping began. The studio manager was supervising the camera line-up, his headphones crackling with instructions from the show's director—a man called Peter Craddock, who was firmly under Dick Hunt's thumb.

Dick Hunt used to do his own 'warm-ups', which was unusual in television—most shows used someone else, not the star of the show—to do it. What it meant was that about five minutes before the programme was due to start taping, Dick would come out, and chat to the studio audience. He would tell them who the guest was that evening, and generally relax people so that when the show started, their reactions would be quicker—they would applaud, laugh, whatever, and participate in the programme. Katy guessed why Hunt made a practice of doing his own warm-ups. He wanted the studio audience on his side before he began a show. Sometimes, when he had very famous guests, who were well used to appearing on television, they too knew the tricks of winning over a studio audience. But Katy didn't expect Laurence Martineau to be able to do that; nor did she think, somehow, that he would want to.

At seven-twenty, Dick appeared. He did a masterly job. There were oohs and aahs when he announced that the guest was to be Laurence Martineau. Dick played them along. He built Laurence Martineau up, and then reminded his audience that he had never been interviewed before. He hinted that there might be some surprises coming—just enough to whet everyone's appetite. Then he seated himself, clipboard on his lap, in a tilting chair camera left, and the lights went down. The studio manager explained to the audience when they must clap, and showed them the red applause card he would hold up, standing behind camera. People shuffled and whispered. The atmosphere was electric with excitement.

The countdown was beginning in the producer's box, and

Katy could see Peter Craddock's thin face nervously peering at monitors behind his soundproof glass panel. He cued in sound, and the show's familiar racy introduction music began. Then the studio manager's arm came down, the lights went up, and the red light on one of the cameras came on, as it angled in on Dick Hunt's impeccably bronzed features.

'Good evening, hello, glad to have you with us. The show this evening marks a rather special event, and a departure from our normal format. This evening I have only one guest with me, and I think you'll understand why that is when I tell you that the guest is . . . Laurence Martineau.'

The cue card came up. Gasps and applause from the studio audience. Dick raised a hand in a modest gesture, let the clapping run on, and cut it off at precisely the right moment like a conductor with an orchestra. He smiled his wide, insincere smile that came across so well on screen.

'I don't really think Mr Martineau needs any introduction from me. He has been called, as you will all know, our greatest classical actor. Those of you who may have missed his Shakespearean performances . . .' there was a slight pause to allow for a ripple of laughter from the audience, '. . . will have certainly seen his many films. You will also know, I think, that Laurence Martineau does not give interviews, and so this programme is by way of being a first. A great honour for us all, and so, without more ado . . . Laurence Martineau!'

The show's theme music started up again, the lights hit the entrance at the back of the set, the camera operator swung the camera round on its trolley, there was a momentary pause, and then Laurence Martineau appeared at the top of the small flight of steps, tall, dark, totally composed. The audience burst into wild applause before the cue card even came up, and there were audible sighs of adulation from some of the women in the studio. The camera tracked Laurence Martineau as he came down the stairs, shook Dick Hunt's hand, and seated himself in the other brown suede chair camera right.

Dick went into his usual routine of welcoming a guest, flattering, putting at ease.

'Well now, Mr Martineau—no, I can't call you that. May I call you Laurence, or even . . .' sideways glance at the audience, '. . . Larry?'

Laurence Martineau gave him an easy smile, and let his

eyes turn momentarily to the audience.

'But of course,' he said drily, 'no one else does, but I should be delighted. It's a novelty.'

There was a ripple of laughter, and Dick Hunt looked discomfited for a fraction of a second.

Katy felt some of her tension subside, and her hands—which must have clenched involuntarily when Laurence Martineau came on—relaxed.

The next half hour went well. Dick Hunt asked good, but innocuous, questions. He was a good listener, and he drew Laurence Martineau out. He talked about his childhood, and Katy learned a lot about him which had not been in the cuttings. That his mother had been French, his father English. That he had been brought up in France, but educated at a Spartan English public school. That his grandfather had been the famous Victorian actor-manager Sir Herbert Martineau, but that his father—an engineer—had opposed his becoming an actor. Laurence Martineau was charming, relaxed, witty. Katy listened to him, fascinated. How could anyone who had never done an interview before be so cool, so good at handling the situation? The audience loved him, and Dick Hunt was playing along—keeping the questions light, encouraging the anecdotes. But he was giving Laurence Martineau rope—Katy knew that. The tough questions would come later.

Dick moved the questions on. They covered the early performances, the first leading roles. Katy looked quickly at her watch. Nearly forty-five minutes of the programme were over already. When was Hunt going to switch tactics?

She saw the studio manager give Dick Hunt a cue, and he came in at the end of Martineau's next answer.

'Right, well, this is all fascinating. We'll take a break now, and we'll be back in a few moments to talk about the watershed in your career, when you played Hamlet. Back in a few moments . . .'

The studio lights dimmed for the commercial break, and a make-up girl rushed on to touch up Dick's make-up. Laurence Martineau sipped a glass of water, and Katy saw his eyes move lazily up over the studio audience. They ran along the rows of seats, and then his gaze seemed to rest; he was looking directly at her, Katy realised suddenly. She felt her cheeks blaze hotly, and at once Martineau looked away. He gave no sign that he had seen or recognised her. Lindy came over, and crouched down beside Katy at the end of the row.

'Isn't he amazing? What a man! It's going marvellously, don't you think?'

'Marvellously,' Katy said abstractedly, wishing Lindy would go away.

'That voice! And those eyes! He could come and read the telephone directory to me any night.'

'Why don't you suggest it?' Katy said coolly, for Lindy was irritating her.

'I think I might,' she giggled. 'But I rather gather that since his divorce he's shown very little interest in young ladies. Still, I could impress him with my vast store of knowledge about English Literature, don't you think?'

She laughed again, and went back to her seat. Katy was left wondering quite why she should find that idea so annoying. The theme music started up again, the lights came on, and Dick Hunt consulted his clipboard quickly. His tongue passed wetly over his lips, then he turned to smile at the cameras. Katy's instincts told her that if he was going to start getting tough, it would be soon.

She was right. He began gently enough, talking about that production of *Hamlet*.

'And your Ophelia then was a young actress called Camilla Drew, I think?' he said sweetly, and Katy knew the moment had come - he had his entrée.

She saw Laurence Martineau tense slightly, and so did the rest of the audience. The atmosphere heightened, and the tension was electric.

'Yes, that's correct.'

'Whom you subsequently married?'

'Yes.'

'And subsequently, forgive me, divorced?'

'I was divorced. I did not instigate the proceedings.'

'You were the guilty party, in other words?'

'That is the rather antiquated way in which the laws of our country describe it. Yes.'

'The marriage was not, unfortunately, as successful as your career?'

Laurence Martineau's mouth had set in a hard line, but the body remained completely relaxed and at ease. After that first tiny gesture, not even his hands tensed, and Katy found herself admiring his self-control.

'I don't think that one can sum up five years of one's life quite so precisely, do you?' he said easily.

'I think most people know whether their marriage is a success or not,' Dick Hunt countered. 'I speak, of course, as an untried bachelor.' He gave a half-smile to the audience, and was rewarded with a ripple of laughter. 'Shall we put it this way—it was an acrimonious divorce, was it not?'

'The newspapers certainly did their best to make it one.'

'You mean that it was really quite amicable?'

'I don't think that any action of that kind can be quite amicable, do you? It's bound to be painful, for both parties.'

'So why do you think it happened, Larry? Looking back now, with hindsight? Was it a conflict of careers? You were an ambitious young actor?'

Laurence Martineau smiled. 'Oh, I think all young actors are ambitious,' he said. 'It's something you grow out of. Hopefully.' The audience laughed again, and Katy felt glad. They were still on his side.

'Would you say you were an easy man to live with—I mean, you must know your reputation. You have a hot temper— there was that episode with a newspaper photographer, whose camera you once smashed . . .'

'Oh, I think I'm impossible to live with,' he said easily, almost lazily. 'I wouldn't recommend anyone to do it.'

Katy saw his eyes flick up to the rows of studio seats, and for a moment she thought he looked directly at her, though she couldn't be certain. She felt glad as the studio audience rippled with laughter again, and some of the women sighed audibly.

'Your ex-wife once described you as—and I quote—"a passionate Puritan. Passionate about his work". Do you think that was an accurate assessment?'

'I suppose it is true to say that I am passionate about my work, yes. I have experienced other passions as well, however.' Laurence Martineau smiled, the long mouth lifting in a sensuous curve. There was no doubt in Katy's mind that his passions were by no means confined to his work. The women in the audience sighed again, and Dick Hunt looked a little irritable: so far he had failed to draw blood.

'If you are so passionate about your work, Laurence,' he said silkily, 'then could you tell us why it's over five years since you last worked in the theatre? Since the time of your divorce, in fact?'

This time there was no question that Laurence Martineau was angered; his eyes flashed, and his face darkened. There was a fractional pause.

'I've been making films,' he said finally.

'But you told us all earlier, Laurence, that you much preferred working on the stage— so why have you given it up—since your divorce?'

'I have not given up the stage—I think that's misleading. I have simply been engaged in other work in a different medium,' he said stiffly.

'But you've been engaged in that other work, as you put it, since your divorce. Did that event influence your decision in some way? Psychologically perhaps. Loss of confidence?'

'My divorce had nothing to do with my decision to work in films for a while,' Laurence Martineau said sharply, 'and my confidence is the same as it has always been. Strong in rehearsal, low when I'm standing in the wings.'

'But I understand that you've turned down a lot of theatre offers, Laurence, two from the National Theatre just in the last year.'

'I already had film commitments.' He was stalling, Katy thought, stalling quite well, but nevertheless it was apparent to everyone in the audience that he did not like the line of questioning.

'The decision was nothing to do with the fact that your ex-wife, Camilla Drew, would also have been appearing in those productions?'

There was a sharp intake of breath from several people in the audience. It was the kind of nasty trick Dick usually played, Katy thought, and she wondered who had given him that information. Her palms felt damp again, and she waited to hear how Laurence Martineau would extricate himself from that one.

He did it superbly. He paused for a second, then smiled that easy, bewitching smile again.

'Well now,' he said, leaning forward to Dick Hunt conspiratorially, 'shall we just say that if the cast had included my future wife, rather than my last wife, I might possibly have been more inclined to negotiate . . .'

There was a wave of laughter, and Kate saw Dick Hunt look down at his clipboard rather desperately. *He didn't know Laurence Martineau was planning to remarry*, Katy thought, and she felt cold and somehow hard inside. So that was it— and Dick Hunt hadn't known—his precious research had let him down.

Dick decided to play it the only way he could—clearly he couldn't pretend to know about this and get away with it.

'Hey, now here's a revelation,' he said, grinning widely at the audience. 'That's going to make an awful lot of women very unhappy, Larry. Can you tell us who the fortunate lady is to be?'

'Certainly not,' Laurence Martineau drawled. 'As you may have noticed, I prefer to keep my private life private. Besides, too much publicity might spoil my chances.'

He got a spontaneous round of applause at that, and Katy saw a look of irritation flit briefly across Dick Hunt's face. His quarry had eluded him, and he knew it. There were only a few minutes of the programme left, and he made no attempt to press Laurence Martineau any further. He led the questions back to more general areas, and rounded the programme off in the usual way.

Afterwards, Katy saw Lindy making towards her, but she didn't want to talk. For some reason she still felt irritable and depressed, and, now that the programme was over, there was a sense of anticlimax as well. She dodged out of one of the side doors, and feeling very tired, made for her office. Well, that's that, she thought. She wondered who it was that Laurence Martineau was going to marry, and then crossly dismissed such thoughts from her mind. What business of hers was it anyway? Let the gossip columns have fun with it tomorrow. She would go and collect her things and go home to bed, she thought wearily.

Just as she reached the stairs up to her office, she saw Dick Hunt and Laurence Martineau approaching at the end of the corridor, Dick's pudgy arm firmly around his shoulders. Dick's loud voice reached her on the stairs. 'Great, Laurence, great. What a show! Wait till that goes out on the air tomorrow . . . a pleasure and a privilege. And what about that news you sprang on me at the last moment, crafty timing, never seen anything like it ... Tell me, in confidence, now we're off the air, is that the lucky lady who's your mystery guest at dinner tonight?'

Feeling a little sick, Katy hurried up the stairs, hoping they hadn't seen her. She had no wish to speak to either of them tonight. They reached the bottom of the stairs just as she was about to turn into her office at the top.

'Miss Sutcliffe!'

The cool, powerful voice stopped her in her tracks, and she stopped and turned. Dich Hunt and Laurence Martineau stood at the bottom looking up. Martineau's face wore a mocking smile.

'My mystery guest, Mr Hunt,' he said, and gestured in Katy's direction. 'Sorry to disappoint you. Miss Sutcliffe, I regret I didn't have the chance to ask you earlier. Would you join me for dinner tonight?'

CHAPTER THREE

KATY stood for a moment dumbfounded. She saw Dick Hunt's jaw sag in surprise, and felt a momentary wild elation. But it was succeeded quickly by anger. What was Laurence Martineau playing at? How dared he just assume that he could ask her at the last minute like this, and think that she would have nothing better to do, that she would docilely tag along, like some actor's groupie?

'I'm sorry,' she said stiffly, 'I'm afraid it's not possible. I hope you all have a pleasant evening.' And she turned away quickly and went into her office, closing the door firmly, so there was no possibility of a reply.

Once there, she took her time gathering her things together, so that with any luck Martineau and Hunt would leave the building before she had to go downstairs again.

Finally, after about ten minutes had passed, she felt safe. She put on her jacket, picked up her bag and papers, and went to the door. She had just switched off all the lights, so that the room was lit dimly only by the corridor lights outside that filtered through the glass partitions, when the door suddenly opened. Katy was startled, and audibly caught her breath. A tall, dark figure stood silhouetted in the doorway, and instinctively she backed away. Laurence Martineau came into the room, and closed the door behind him.

'I'm sorry—I startled you,' he said, his voice low. He did not turn on the lights.

'That's all right. I was just going home,' she said involuntarily, and then cursed herself for being so slow-witted. Now she couldn't pretend that she was going out on a previous engagement.

'I want you to come tonight,' he said, almost fiercely, crossing towards her.

'I've told you,' she said, trying to keep her voice calm, 'I can't come.'

'You're going home to some pressing engagement?' He

smiled that mocking smile, and Katy felt a wave of anger.

'If you'd wanted me to join you, I'm afraid you should have asked me earlier. What happened?' she asked. 'Did someone else let you down?' The words came out as a taunt, and even as she said them, she knew they sounded petty and stupid.

'No, no one else let me down,' he said gravely. 'There's no one else I wanted to accompany me.'

He had reached her side, and she looked up into that dark face, and those troubled eyes. She was aware of how tall he was, and how powerful, and she had to fight back the desire to say at once that yes, of course she would go with him. He looked quietly down into her face for some moments, then he reached across and took her arm—rather formally, with a gentle touch that sent fire through her whole body.

'Katharine,' he said, 'I can't explain now, but please, will you come with me? I shan't ask you again, if you refuse.'

She hesitated, doubtful, thrown into confusion to hear her first name on his lips. And then something in her, some instinct, made her suddenly make a leap of trust—she wanted to go anyway. Why not?

'Very well,' she said.

He smiled, and his face seemed to light up with a delight which surprised her.

'Thank you,' he said. 'I think my secretary has arranged a car for me—it should be downstairs. I can drive you to the restaurant, and I'll make sure you get home safely afterwards . . .'

Immediately Katy felt a little alarmed again, 'I mustn't be too late,' she muttered.

'By midnight, if you like,' he said. 'But don't worry—the car won't turn into a pumpkin if we're late . . .' He took her by the arm, and led her from the room, her pulses and her thoughts racing.

Why was he doing this? she wondered. From anyone else she would have thought it was a predictable seduction routine, but this man was different. She didn't think somehow that he would behave in that way. She wished very much that she had time to change, but that was impossible. They walked down the corridors and out of the almost deserted building by a side door.

'To forestall the autograph-hunters,' said Laurence

Martineau, ushering her quickly outside.

By the door was parked a beautiful silver grey Mercedes S.L. convertible. He helped Katy inside, and then got in himself.

'I wish we were in Provence,' he said, 'and that we were going to a little country inn that I know, where there are no fashionable people, and the food is superb. However, I gather it's Angelo's. Dick Hunt has gone on ahead.'

'Don't you like smart London restaurants?' she asked nervously. 'I should have thought you would go to them all the time.'

He gave her a sideways glance, as the engine roared into life.

'Then you would be quite wrong,' he said. 'I detest them.'

'Even after a performance? I would have thought . . .'

'Especially after a performance. I prefer to go home. When I had a home here, that is. Now, of course, I usually manage to avoid London altogether. I find Provence infinitely preferable.'

'I don't know Provence at all,' said Katy, feeling very self-conscious and naïve, and trying to make conversation. 'Is it very beautiful?'

'Very,' he said shortly. 'Tiny remote villages inland—I live about fifty kilometres from Cannes—the house belonged to my mother's family, and it has the advantage of being both beautiful and inaccessible.'

It should suit you, then, Katy thought to herself, for she was very aware of how guarded he was. She wondered why he put these barriers around himself, and who he allowed to breach them—not many people, she imagined. The lovely Camilla Drew, of course, and now this woman he was planning to marry. Was she French? she wondered, and instantly imagined some cool haughty beauty, in elegant couture clothes. She sighed, and he glanced quickly across at her, his lean sculptured profile etched against the passing street lamps.

'You're tired,' he said.

'No, not really. I was just wishing I was more suitably dressed for this expedition.'

'Don't be ridiculous,' he said sharply. 'I detest women who fish for compliments.'

'I wasn't doing any such thing!' she said hotly, and glared at him.

'I hope not,' he said quietly, and they drove the rest of the
way to Soho in silence, his face closed and unreadable, hers
tight-lipped with annoyance. Her nervousness was increasing,
she thought; half of her wished she had not come, half still
rejoiced in the adventure.

They reached Angelo's late, at about a quarter past ten.
The whole place was buzzing with activity, and was very
crowded. Katy had never been anywhere so fashionable and
expensive before, and looked around her curiously as they
went in. A waiter ushered them obsequiously down a spiral
staircase, and into a huge arched, white-painted cellar. Large
modern paintings hung on the walls, and the white tablecloths
and cutlery gleamed in the light of hundreds of candles. At the
bottom of the stairs stood a table laid out with a beautiful
display of fruits, vegetables and cold hors-d'oeuvres. A trolley
groaned under the weight of sumptuous and elaborate des-
serts—great confections of pastry and chocolate and cream
and spun sugar and fruit. A third had shellfish, oysters, lobsters and crabs, all exquisitely displayed and laid out on beds
of ice.

The room was hot, loud with conversation, heavy with
cigarette smoke. There were men in black ties, and men in
jeans with shirts open to the waist, their necks looped with
chains and jewellery. The women were equally diverse—some
wore expensive dresses, diamonds, silks, and had bared
bronzed shoulders. Some wore aggressively fashionable
understated things. They passed a spectacular black woman,
her hair drawn back severely from her fine boned face, who
was wearing dungarees which barely covered her breasts, and
no shirt. As soon as they entered there was a pause in the
general conversation, heads turned in their direction, and there
was then a buzz of recognition.

'It's Laurence Martineau,' Katy heard one woman whisper
as the waiter shepherded them past her table.

'Who's that with him?' whispered her companion.

'Some lucky little dolly bird,' Katy heard, and her cheeks
flushed with shame and anger.

Dick Hunt had the best table in the room—predictably. It
was right at the far end, and they had to walk a gauntlet of
stares to reach it. Katy felt even worse when they got there.
Dick and Peter Craddock stood up to greet them, and she

noted they had changed into dinner jackets. They were accompanied by two women, neither of whom she knew. Dick's companion was wearing a silk dress that plunged almost to her navel, and a rope of thick gold and pearls around her long, tanned neck. Her artfully streaked blonde hair cascaded in loose waves over her slender shoulders. Peter Craddock was not with his wife—but that wasn't surprising, he rarely was. His guest that evening was a black girl with an American accent. She was very tall and very thin; she wore her hair in a spectacular Afro, the resulting halo pinned with gauze butterflies. Her dress was fine embroidered silk, transparent, probably from Thea Porter's, and probably costing the earth. Katy had never felt frumpier and worse dressed in her life. She saw the two women's eyes rake her clothes, and run contemptuously over her thick tousled hair. They glanced away with a smirk of satisfaction at each other, and she guessed what they were thinking—'Not much competition there'.

'Larry!' said Dick Hunt effusively, and loudly. He drew back a chair beside him and ignored Katy completely.

Laurence Martineau frowned slightly, and ignoring Dick Hunt's obvious wish that he should sit next to him, he stood back, and helped Katy into the waiting chair. Dick Hunt looked annoyed, then made an effort to be polite.

'Katy, sweetie,' he said, 'what a pleasant surprise! So Laurence persuaded you after all. Now—Laurence, this is Peter whom you've already met, of course, and this is Cindy,' indicating the black girl, 'and this is Tanya. You'll know their faces from the posters, of course . . .'

'Will I?' said Laurence Martineau. 'Tanya and Cindy, may I introduce Katharine Sutcliffe, who works for Mr Hunt on his programme?'

Cindy giggled. 'Hey,' she said, 'I really love these formal English manners, you know what I mean?'

'Do you?' said Laurence Martineau drily. 'Well, they probably seem a little old-fashioned, but I think they have their advantage.'

Dick Hunt took over the stage management of the meal. The others had already been drinking while they waited, and there were already two empty bottles of wine on the table. Loudly Dick Hunt called the wine waiter and ordered more.

but when the menus were brought he waved them aside.

'Now, I want you all to put yourselves in my hands. We're going to have a real celebration tonight—Angelo, have you laid on the caviare I ordered?' The owner of the restaurant bowed and scraped, and a vast pot of Iranian caviare duly arrived. The waiters fussed around bringing lemons, chopped egg, chopped onions, blinis, and black bread.

'Blinis and caviare in an Italian restaurant?' Laurence Martineau raised his eyebrows.

'Sure,' said Dick Hunt expansively. 'Gotta do the thing properly—Angelo will lay on anything for me, won't you, Angelo?'

The small Italian nodded nervously, his eyes flicking over his fleets of waiters, making sure they didn't upset the great Dick Hunt.

'Best caviare in the world,' Dick Hunt announced expansively.

'Best in the world,' echoed Peter Craddock dutifully.

'Like it, Laurence? Better than Russian these days, don't you think?'

'I eat it so rarely that I can hardly make the comparison.'

Dick Hunt gave one of his flat laughs, which failed to sound jovial. 'Poor old Laurence, what a hard luck story—was it a million pence or a million pounds you were paid for your last picture?'

Laurence Martineau ignored the remark, and Tanya seized the opportunity to impress upon him how much she admired his work.

'I mean I think it's really just marvellous,' she said, in a low breathy voice. 'That part you played in *Vagabond Heroes*, you were so *sexy*.' She fluttered her eyelashes, and leaned forward so that her low neckline sagged even further. 'Of course, it's always been my ambition to work in the movies, I'm taking voice lessons just at present . . .'

'Oh, but that was nothing, sweetie,' Dick patted her hand proprietorially. 'His films are O.K.—but you should see him on the stage . . .'

Tanya smiled sweetly. 'Oh, Dick darling, I guess I'm a little too young . . .'

The rising annoyance Katy had been feeling ever since they

arrived now spilled over. She was fuming at the whole atmosphere of cheapness and vulgarity.

'How old are you?' she said to Tanya coldly.

Cindy giggled rapturously. 'Oh my,' she said, 'get that! Some question!'

'Don't you know ladies never discuss their ages, sweetie?' said Dick, though Katy could see malicious amusement in his eyes.

'Do they not?' she said. 'Well, I'm twenty-three, and I first saw Mr Martineau on the stage when I was fourteen, so I don't see the difficulty.'

Tanya's cheeks coloured slightly under her heavy make-up. Katy reckoned that she was probably a good three or four years older, twenty-seven at least, and clearly the remark annoyed her.

'Who is this baby girl you've hired, Dick?' she drawled. '*Mr* Martineau—I mean, she's too quaint!'

'Saw him at fourteen, and been carrying a torch for him ever since, I'll bet,' said Dick Hunt. 'You're a lucky man, Laurence. You know what we call Katy around the studios? Little Miss Iceberg, that's what. I guess it takes a *very* famous actor to crack that English reserve . . .'

Laurence Martineau's mouth had set in a straight line, and Katy could sense his anger.

'I can imagine no higher compliment, in your studios, than that particular nickname,' he said coolly, his voice cutting across Cindy and Tanya's giggles.

'Oh. Why?' said Peter Craddock thickly. He was getting drunk, and attempting belligerence.

'I should have thought it was obvious,' said Laurence Martineau.

Further sparring was luckily interrupted by the arrival of more food. There was veal, roasted with rosemary and wine, and enormous dishes of fettuccine, decorated with white truffles.

The truffles provided Dick Hunt with the opportunity to discourse at some length about their cost, how they were flown into Angelo's every morning from Tuscany, how they were infinitely preferable to black truffles, and so on and so forth.

Laurence Martineau and Katy were quite silent; two more

bottles of wine had been consumed, and the talk became freer, ranging in a gossipy way over past guests and programmes. Peter Craddock was being more than a little indiscreet, Katy thought, and it was no surprise to her, as they were provided with yet more wine, and the dessert trolley arrived, that Dick Hunt chose to change the subject.

'Well, Laurence,' he said, lighting up one of his endless cigarettes, and puffing smoke in Katy's face. 'It was a terrific programme, a real honour. Now you'll be going back to France, I imagine?'

'In a few days' time, yes.'

'I hear it's some house you've got over there in Provence.'

'Oh, is that what you hear?' Katy saw an odd glance pass between them, as if they knew each other rather better than she had assumed. Then Dick pressed on:

'Some kind of castle, I hear—towers, a moat, that sort of thing.'

'Really?' Laurence Martineau gave him a look of such contempt and loathing, it would have annihilated a more sensitive man. It was as if they were playing some private game, Katy thought. 'You make it sound too grand,' Laurence went on. 'It has towers, yes, but it's not really a chateau—it's a fortified manor house, it dates from the fifteenth century.'

'Wow!' exclaimed Cindy. 'Like, living history, you know what I mean? What a thrill! You know, I'd really like to see that,' she said, smiling beguilingly. 'I have a modelling trip to Nice next month, and I guess it's not far from there.'

'I'm afraid I don't encourage visitors,' he said courteously. 'When I'm there, I like to be alone so that I can work.'

'What's this place of yours called, Laurence?'

'It's called La Bayardière,' he said shortly.

There was an interruption as everyone began to choose a pudding from the dessert trolley, and in the middle of the argument, Laurence Martineau turned to Katy.

'You said you don't know Provence, I think?'

'No, I don't,' she said. 'Your house sounds beautiful. And it has a very romantic name.'

He smiled. 'I was very lucky to inherit it. My mother's brother died without issue, and I inherited it through my mother when she died about ten years ago.'

'Did you go and live there at once?' she asked. 'I suppose

you couldn't really, because you were working in London.'

A shadow passed across his face. 'No,' he said, 'my wife didn't like France. I went to live there after we parted.'

He looked sad when he said this, and Katy remembered the pain he had spoken of in connection with his divorce on the programme. Obviously he had been very much in love with Camilla Drew, she thought. Maybe he still was—the divorce had been brought by her.

Dick Hunt had obviously been eavesdropping on the conversation, because he leaned across to them and interrupted.

'And you know he inherited the title as well, don't you, Katy? He's the Comte de la Bayardière, I believe—but he doesn't like it mentioned.'

'A Count?' cried Cindy, laying a plate of profiteroles heavily heaped with cream before her. 'A genuine Count? Hey, what a thrill! It's too much, you know, a real live French Count!'

'I can't see what's so thrilling,' said Tanya petulantly. 'Have you never met a Count before? You must move in very narrow circles.'

'I don't use the title,' said Laurence Martineau. 'Most titles, particularly French ones, are ridiculous. It usually means that one of your ancestors pimped for Napoleon.'

Dick Hunt ordered coffee, and brandies, and a waiter passed around Corona cigars. Katy noticed that Peter Craddock was now extremely drunk, and that even Dick Hunt, who had a hard head for liquor, was drunker than usual. For some reason, his drinking made him turn his attention to her, which was the last thing she wanted.

He kept pouring her more coffee and pressing her to have a Cognac.

'Isn't Katy a sweetie?' he announced to the table at large, when she refused another drink for the third time. 'A girl who knows her own mind. I can't tell you what an asset she is on the programme. Best little researcher I've had for years, can charm the birds off the trees, she can. Oh, she's not always as quiet as she is tonight. Why, when we had James Conrad, you know—the novelist—on the show, and a more cantankerous s.o.b. I can't remember, it was little Katy that talked to him, soothed him, set him up for me beautifully, she did.'

Katy felt Laurence Martineau stiffen in his chair beside her, and he turned to her with a look of enquiry in his eyes. She blushed deeply, wondering how she could get away, or shut Dick up, but he pressed on unstoppably.

'And she's so hard on me. Plays hard to get, says she will have a little nice intimate supper with me, then says she won't. What am I going to do with you, Katy sweetie?'

He reached across with one of his pudgy hands, and ruffled her hair, then let his arm fall across her shoulders so that he could fondle her and draw her to him.

She was desperately embarrassed, and also very angry. What would Laurence Martineau think of her now? She managed to move Dick's hand firmly aside, and with shaking legs stood up. The scene at their table was attracting quite a lot of attention, and all heads were turned in their direction, Katy realised. Very deliberately, she looked at her watch. It was nearly one a.m.

'I'm sorry,' she said, 'I shall have to go home now. It's getting late, and I have to work in the morning.'

Laurence Martineau also stood up, and she blessed him silently.

'I'll drive you home,' he said, and took her arm in a fierce grip above the elbow. He looked extremely angry, she thought.

She thanked Dick for dinner as quickly as she could, but there was no getting away so easily. First he insisted that Laurence must stay—they had so much to talk about . . . Katy could go home in a cab . . .

'There were things I wanted to talk about too,' said Laurence Martineau in a cold voice, in which the dislike was unmistakable. 'But now is not the moment. And I shall certainly see Miss Sutcliffe home.'

'Have a good time, kiddies,' said Dick, leering at both of them. 'You've got taste, Laurence, I'll say that for you. Always could recognise class when you saw it, never went for the window dressings——' he gestured at Tanya and Cindy, who were watching this scene open-mouthed. 'I'd take this little sweetie back to her bed-sitter any time, but you're the lucky man. Just remember, though—Little Miss Iceberg, we call her. Still, you'll be able to melt her, no doubt. Just the way you did Camilla . . .'

Laurence Martineau moved so swiftly that Katy hardly saw

what happened. One moment he was beside her, holding her arm, the next he had stepped forward with the grace and speed of a panther. His arm came back, and his fist smacked into Dick Hunt's jaw in a perfect upper cut. Hunt seemed to be lifted in the air by the force of the blow. He rose, and then fell spreadeagled backwards. As he went, he grabbed at the table, pulling it back on top of him. He hit the ground in a heap as glass, silver, plates, cream, sugar, strawberries and chocolate profiteroles cannoned to the floor with a crash. There was a moment's stunned and total silence in the restaurant. Laurence Martineau gripped Katy's arm so tightly that it hurt, and propelled her towards the door.

Angelo, the owner, was standing there, his mouth open in amazement, his eyes popping in disbelief that this could happen to the great Dick Hunt, and in his restaurant. Nobody moved, and no one attempted to stop them leaving, Katy noted. Everyone seemed paralysed by the incident.

Laurence Martineau stopped opposite Angelo, who cowered backwards as if afraid he might have earned the same treatment.

'Send me the bill for the damage,' he said curtly. 'Oh, and fire the chef who made the blinis. Alternatively, hire a Russian.' Then he marched Katy up the stairs, still holding her arm, his face grim. The Mercedes was parked outside the entrance to the restaurant. He opened the door.

'Get in,' he said tersely.

He was inside, and revving the engine, before Katy knew what was happening, and within seconds they were streets away. The whole thing had happened in two minutes, and Katy felt completely overwhelmed. Laurence Martineau, to knock Dick Hunt out, at a table at London's most fashionable restaurant! Tomorrow it would be all over the papers, she thought—not that she cared about that. But she felt sickened by the whole evening, by the bitchiness and ugliness of the conversation, the cheapness of everyone's behaviour except Laurence Martineau's. She had never seen a man hit another man before, and she hadn't exactly liked it. But on the other hand, Dick Hunt had been so rude, so insufferably rude . . . She felt upset, but also excited, she realised. It was rather as if a knight had ridden up on a white charger . . .

Laurence Martineau did not say a word. He was driving the car fast, past the Ritz and towards Green Park. His hands were tight on the steering wheel, and he drove with absolute concentration. When they reached Hyde Park Corner, he drew up at the intersection.

'I suppose you'd better tell me where you live,' he said brusquely, almost as if he had totally forgotten her presence in the car. 'For all I know, I'm going in completely the wrong direction.'

'I live in Little Venice,' she said, trying to keep her voice steady. 'In Aubrey Crescent. If you go up Park Lane, and then . . .'

'I know the way, thank you,' he said curtly, and the car accelerated away again, the tyres screeching in protest as he rounded the corner at speed.

He drove up Park Lane and on without hesitation. At the canal basin at the top of Warwick Avenue he turned left, and pulled the car up abruptly by the water.

'Aubrey Crescent is straight on,' Katy said nervously.

'I know exactly where Aubrey Crescent is,' he said, 'and I shall deliver you back there shortly, don't worry. Meanwhile, I want to talk to you, and we may as well walk.'

Before she had time to reply, he had got out and was round to her side of the car, holding the door open. There seemed no point in protesting, so she climbed out.

'Right, we'll go down here.'

There was a small towpath that led along the side of the canal, and followed it as it wound through London. Farther along there were barges, and overhanging willow trees. But the towpath had a gate, which—Katy knew—was usually kept locked in the daytime—always at night.

They walked down the steps, and along the path until they reached the gate, and then stopped. It was very beautiful—a clear night, with the stars all visibly stretched across the sky, and a full moon shining down and reflecting on the water. It was utterly still; the only sound was the water lapping at the edges of the path.

'Still locked? It always was. Come here.'

Before she could protest, his arms were around her, and his strong grip lifted her easily over to the other side of the gate. He climbed over it, and vaulted down beside her.

'I don't really think that we're supposed to . . .' Katy began.

'Of course we're not supposed to. But I don't intend to let the killjoys of the Inland Waterways Board dictate to me whether or not I shall walk along here. I've known this place since I was a boy, and it's one of the few places in London they haven't yet managed to spoil.'

She felt nervous and upset, and the sudden swift pressure of his body against hers had done nothing to compose her. She felt a mass of conflicting emotions—anger that he should take control of her in this way, but also an insidious attraction, which she could feel pulsing through her body, and fought to deny.

They walked along the path for some minutes in silence. It was utterly deserted there. On one side of them were high walls, on the other the water. Katy looked around her, trying to be calm, trying not to think about this dark strange man who walked beside her, trying not to think about the extraordinary sequence of events which had begun that morning when she first met him at the airport. Finally, attempting to make her voice sound firm, she said, 'I think you should say what you came to say, and that then I should go home, don't you?'

'Very well.'

They had come to a bench on the side of the towpath, and they sat down. There was silence. Laurence Martineau did not even look at her, but stared down into the water.

'You've made me very angry,' he said finally.

'*I've* made you angry?' she exclaimed indignantly, instantly on the defensive. 'I rather had the impression you were angry with Dick.'

'Oh, I was,' he said. 'I don't make a habit of hitting other men on the jaw, in spite of what the press writes. But Dick Hunt and I certainly have scores to settle.'

'You mean the programme?' Katy felt confused. 'But I thought you handled it so well. He was offensive, but he got nowhere.'

Laurence Martineau hardly seemed to hear her words, and again she had the impression that his thoughts were far away from her, locked into some private memory. He sat still, his eyes shaded, his body tense beside her on the bench.

'No, it wasn't that,' he said finally. 'I hit him because of what he said about you.'

'And your wife,' Katy added quickly, and then could have bitten off her tongue.

He rounded on her, his eyes blazing. '*Not* that,' he said fiercely. 'You don't know what you're talking about. He insulted you. He'd been insulting you all evening. And that made me angry—with him and with you.'

'Why with me?'

'Because he doesn't really matter. He and his kind are vermin—no, worse than that. The kind of thing that crawls out covered in slime when you pick up a stone. But sooner or later Dick Hunt will be finished, and people will forget him. He's insignificant—nasty but insignificant. But you . . .'

He was looking directly into her eyes now, and again Katy felt that weakening sensation she had felt that morning in the car. It made her feel odd and also desperate, as if there weren't enough time and she somehow had to say a million things to him, all of which whirled uncontrollably in her head.

'Why do you work for him?' he said angrily. 'How can you bring yourself to do it?'

She felt suddenly sick and ashamed, because she knew he was right—had known the truth of what he said from almost her first day at the studios.

'How do you feel, Katharine Sutcliffe, charming people, "setting them up", as your employer so charmingly puts it, getting them to relax so they can go on a programme in front of fifteen million people and make fools of themselves? Have their whole lives raked over by his grubby fingers, be tried and proven guilty? You approve of all that? How many people, do you think, lead such blameless lives that they could go on that programme with a safe conscience?'

Katy turned away from the relentless gaze fixed on her face.

'I don't know, I don't know,' she sighed. 'I have thought of that, obviously I have. But . . . sometimes the programme does expose scandals, cover-ups, things which ought to be exposed, and . . .'

Her voice trailed away. She was not even convincing herself. There was a short silence. She could feel his contempt, and didn't dare to look at him.

'All right,' he said finally, in a different voice, a colder one. 'So—begin at the beginning. Why did you take the job in the first place?'

Katy hesitated. She wanted to tell him, but it might come out like a sob story, special pleading, and she didn't want that.

'Well,' she said carefully, 'my father died three years ago, and we found—that is, my mother found, that there wasn't a lot of money . . .' She paused, but he clearly wasn't going to help her, so she pressed on. 'We have this house, in Suffolk, which is quite old, and costs a lot to run, and my mother wanted to stay there. I have three sisters. The two elder ones are married, and the younger one was still at school—there were her school fees . . .'

'So you thought you'd be the family breadwinner?' His tone was sarcastic, without an ounce of sympathy.

'No,' she said hastily. 'Not exactly. But if I worked it would help a bit. And besides, I . . . I wanted to leave home and be independent. To come to London and earn some money. And this seemed a good job. I don't know. I didn't just want to stay at home and wait to get married. I didn't want to spend the rest of my life as a shorthand-typist . . .'

Her voice was starting to break, and she knew she was close to tears. 'It's all very well for you,' she said angrily. 'You're a man. You had one thing you could do supremely well, and you've done it. I didn't know what I could do. I wanted to find out, before . . .' She broke off.

'Before what?' he asked, more gently.

'Oh, I don't know. Before I gave up and became a wife and mother—all those things.'

Before you settled for Bob, exactly the way everyone predicted, she thought, but she didn't say it.

He looked at her coolly, appraisingly.

'Do you so despise being a wife and mother?' he said, and his tone was so flippant she could have hit him.

'No, I don't,' she said angrily. 'Why do you always misunderstand me? I just didn't want to settle, to stagnate, to take the easy option. Not until I'd seen something of the world, seen what I could do. Can't you understand that?'

'And you call Dick Hunt and his loathesome programme seeing the world, do you?' he said sarcastically. 'I'd have thought the "easy option"—whatever that was—might have been preferable.'

'That's because you know nothing about it!' Katy cried

angrily. 'Why should I have to explain myself to you anyway?
I can work for whom I please, and it's none of your business.
I didn't need you to hit Dick Hunt, and I certainly don't need
this kind of cross-examination. You're treating me like a
child—stop interfering!'

She stood up abruptly, and started back down the path, but
he came after her.

'Leave me alone!' she shouted. 'I can perfectly well walk
home. I know the way, and I don't need you to help me climb
over a damn gate!'

'Katharine!'

He caught her by the arm as she turned on her heel, and
pulled her roughly towards him with an easy strength.
Suddenly she found herself pinioned against the hardness of
his body, and for a moment she felt his heart beating fast
against her own. His head was bent, and his mouth was close
to hers.

'You're a little fool,' he said, and his hands moved up her
back until they cradled her head and hair, and tilted her face
towards him. This can't be happening, she thought wildly, but
she couldn't move. She was held as much by the strange glittering expression in his eyes as by the negligent force of his
arms.

'What a wilful young woman,' he said at last, his voice low
and roughened. 'And well named. You need taming, Kate. Do
you know that?'

'And I suppose you think you could do it?' she replied,
aware that her voice lacked control, that an odd languor and
pleasure was beginning to flood through her body, that she
had no wish to resist.

'Oh, yes,' he said, with great seriousness, 'I could do it. I
could do it, Kate.'

Then, very slowly, with great deliberateness, he bent his
head and kissed her. His mouth was hard against hers, without
gentleness, and he pressed her body tightly against him with
an urgent hunger. Nothing that had ever happened to her had
prepared her for the feelings that suddenly flooded through
her body. Pleasure welled up, a deep pleasure that sucked her
under. The edge of desperation which had been with her all
day suddenly went; and a mad, exhilarating happiness filled
her whole being. For a moment she surrendered completely to

that, and to the nakedness of his want. Then, somehow, her mind began working again. What was she doing? Behaving like a cheap, easy pushover .. With all her force, she thrust him away.

'Don't!' she said fiercely. 'Please, don't.'

He stood in the moonlight looking down at her, still with the same dangerous glittering expression in his eyes, and with a mocking half-smile on his lips.

'I apologise,' he said, in a tone that was unapologetic. 'I brought you here because I wanted to talk to you, not because I planned this—believe me. But I've been fighting off a desire to kiss you rather thoroughly, ever since you stood opposite me in that airport lounge looking slightly dishevelled and extremely angry. Forgive me. I shall take you home.'

And he did. They walked back to the car in silence. He helped Katy over the gate, taking her hand and relinquishing it immediately afterwards.

They got back into the car and drove the few hundred yards to the house where she lived. Laurence Martineau pulled up, and they sat in silence, looking out at the deserted street, the houses pale and ghostly in the light from the street lamps. The whole of London seemed so still that Katy felt he must hear the beating of her heart.

'You were quite right in what you said,' she said finally, stiffly. 'I suppose I've known it for quite a long while. It was just hearing it from ... another person that made me angry. I'm sorry.'

'And you were right too,' he said, his voice sounding cool again, even distant. 'I have no right to interfere. I'm sorry I did. Goodnight, Katharine. Thank you for coming with me. No doubt we shall read amusing accounts of it all in the papers tomorrow. And, as usual, they'll have missed the whole point of the story. Do you have your keys?'

He opened the car door formally for her, and escorted her to the foot of the stone steps that led up to her front door

'Goodnight,' she said hesitantly.

'Goodnight.'

She turned away, went up the steps, and with trembling fingers unlocked the door.

Inside, she shut it behind her, and stood in the dark of the hall, leaning against the cool wall. For a few wild minutes she prayed silently and incoherently. That he would come after her, that she would hear his footsteps, that the bell would ring . . . but there was silence.

Then she heard the Mercedes' engine roar into life, and the car accelerate away down the road. She stood there still, listening to the sound of the engine growing fainter, to the sound of Laurence Martineau driving out of her life. When she could hear it no more she went slowly upstairs to bed.

CHAPTER FOUR

KATY hardly slept all night, and when she did finally fall asleep, the light was already beginning to filter through the curtains, and her dreams were fitful and troubling. She woke to the usual sounds of Jane beginning her endless morning toilette in the bathroom. Katy lay there in bed for a while, staring up at the ceiling, feeling exhausted, and miserable. All she could think of was standing on that towpath, by the dark water, and listening to Laurence Martineau's accusations ... more than anything else, she felt ashamed.

He was right, everything he said she had known in her heart. How could she have gone on with that odious, supposedly glamorous job, gone on working for that horrible man? There was only one good thing which had come out of the previous day, she thought, and that was the realisation that she must resign, leave Dick Hunt and the programme as soon as she could. As she lay there in bed, she suddenly felt quite calm: she had made the decision, now she just had to carry it out.

She couldn't face Jane that morning, so she waited until she was safely out of the flat, then she got up. She played some music, made coffee, had a long, slow bath, and soaked luxuriously in the scented water. She washed her hair, then dried it sitting in the sun by the window. When she dressed, she dressed carefully, putting on one of her prettiest dresses, a longish loose smock, the low neckline threaded with pale blue ribbon. She tied back her hair with the same ribbon, put a turquoise necklace around her neck, and some blue canvas espadrilles on her feet. She looked at her watch—it was nearly eleven, and she should have been at the studios hours ago. Any minute now the telephone would ring, she thought, and it would be Lindy, anxious to find out what had happened last night, and why she wasn't at work that morning. Well, let them wait, she thought. She decided to walk down to the corner shop, buy a newspaper, and see if they were reporting on last night's episode at Angelo's.

Downstairs in the street, the sun was hot, it was like a summer's day, and the warmth made her feel much more cheerful. She walked along the street, trying not to think about Laurence Martineau, trying not to look at the place where his Mercedes had been parked the previous night. When she reached the shop, the first thing she saw outside was two newspaper headlines, blazoned across the front of the papers in the rack.

'Famous actor fells TV star' read one; 'Stars in fight at West End Niterie' read the other. Inside she bought the paper, and glanced down at the front pages. All the tabloids were having a heyday with it. Photographs of Laurence Martineau and Dick Hunt sprawled across the page; the *Daily Mail* had a picture of Tanya, and an interview . . . 'I can't understand what happened, we were having a really nice evening . . .' The *Standard* must have got to the scene first, because they had a picture of Dick Hunt being helped to his feet, surrounded by a chaos of smashed crockery, squashed fruit and pastry, and broken wine glasses. Katy was pleased to note that Dick looked as if he had the beginnings of a black eye, and a trickle of blood ran down his chin from the corner of his mouth.

Back at the flat, she made herself some more coffee, and settled down to read the accounts. Most of them were as inaccurate as Laurence Martineau had predicted, and biased by the fact that Dick Hunt had been only too ready to comment, whereas Laurence Martineau could not be traced. To Katy's relief, she was mentioned in only a couple of papers, which commented that Laurence Martineau had left the restaurant in an angry mood, with beautiful twenty-three-year-old Katy Sutcliffe, a researcher on Dick Hunt's programme. She wondered who had given them that information, though it seemed pretty obvious that it must have been Dick Hunt, or possibly Peter Craddock. News had leaked out of Laurence Martineau's statement on the programme about his future wife, and the gossip columns had latched on to that: one of them had a photograph of him, and three head-shots of well-known movie stars under the headline, 'Fighting it out to be Mrs Martineau the Second'.

Katy stared at their photographs, feeling chill and unhappy, and wondering how accurate the paper was in its assessment of their chances. Then suddenly she felt ashamed again. What was she doing, reading all that rubbish? It was time she put the whole business out of her mind. She would ring up the studios, she thought, and speak to Dick, and tell him she was leaving.

Although she was determined, she still felt terribly nervous as she dialled the number and waited to be put through to Dick's office. There was quite a pause, and then finally Lindy came on the line.

'Oh, Katy, it's you!' she said, and the tone of her voice betrayed the fact that Dick Hunt was in the room with her. 'Why aren't you in? I think Dick wants to speak to you . . .'

Katy heard a familiar voice saying, 'Give me the phone, damn you!' and then Dick Hunt came on the line.

'What the hell do you think you're playing at?' he demanded aggressively, and she noticed that his voice sounded thicker than usual—probably the result of last night's blow on the chin. 'Why weren't you in here first thing this morning? You think just because you get taken out to a fancy restaurant by a fancy actor you can drift in here as and when you please? Well, I've got news for you, baby!'

'I'm not coming in, Dick,' said Katy, making her voice sound as firm and steady as she could.

'Oh, you're not? Well, in that case, sweetie, I'll save you the trouble of turning up Monday. You're fired!'

'I'm resigning, in any case,' Katy said, fighting to keep her voice level. 'I don't want to work on the programme any longer, and in particular I don't want to work for you. So you can just stop bullying.'

There was a silence on the other end of the line, and she could hear him breathing heavily.

'You stupid little tart,' he said finally. 'You come out to a classy restaurant as my guest . . .'

'Laurence Martineau's guest, actually,' she interjected.

'*My* guest. Who do you think picked up the tab after last night's shenanigans? Your handsome actor hero? No way. You go out on the town for the first time in your prissy uptight little existence, you're rude to my guests, then you egg that guy on to start a fight, and waltz out afterwards, without so much as a by-your-leave. Couldn't wait to drag Martineau back to your bedsitter, could you? Was that it, little Miss Iceberg?'

Katy was shaking by this time, but she managed to keep her voice as irritatingly cold as she could make it. 'You're quite wrong,' she said, 'and as usual are making the mistake of judging people by your own sordid standards. So keep your job, Mr Hunt, I'd just like you to know that Laurence Martineau hit you about one minute before I would have done, though no doubt more effectively.'

And she hung up. She cried afterwards, and wasn't quite sure why. Partly because Dick Hunt had been so unpleasant, and it was an ordeal to stand up to him, however much she hated him. Partly because, in her head, she could still hear the sound of Laurence Martineau's Mercedes driving off into the night, and she wondered if he had that effect on many other people's lives, upsetting, disrupting, and changing them so swiftly, and then abruptly departing.

The day seemed to pass very slowly after that. She cleaned the flat, she went to the shops and bought some food. She didn't allow herself to take a walk along the canal towpath, although she knew she wanted to very much. Finally, in the late afternoon, she made some tea, and curled up on the sofa in the sitting room, looking out at the branches of the trees in the garden outside, and went to sleep.

She woke with a start at about five o'clock, feeling stiff and cold. The telephone was ringing, and her heart gave a sudden lurch. Perhaps it was Laurence Martineau, she thought, and reached for the receiver. She heard pips—the call was coming from a telephone kiosk—and then Jane's voice came on the line.

'Hi, Katy? It's Jane. I'm just ringing to say I've got tickets for that rock concert tonight at Earl's Court. Freddie's coming, and we're both going straight on from work. I can get another seat if you want to come—fancy it?'

Katy thanked her, and refused, feeling curiously let down and disappointed. Jane laughed.

'Oh, I suppose a rock concert isn't good enough for you— I've been reading about your exploits last night. No wonder you weren't up this morning! I wondered what had happened. Well, you'll be sorry you missed it . . . don't wait up, we'll be very late. I'm wearing a wonderful silver lamé suit I found in the King's Road this morning, and Freddie's bringing my contact pictures, and he says they're terrific . . . Don't get into any more fights with your glamorous friends! 'Bye ...'

Katy hung up, and as soon as she had replaced the receiver, a black depression settled on her. At least if Jane had been coming home, she could have talked it all over with her, she thought. As it was, the evening stretched before her, empty and miserable, and the enormity of what she had done suddenly hit her. Suddenly she remembered all the bills—bills she had been going to pay with her next month's Metropolitan T.V. cheque. Now there was nothing, and she had hardly any money saved. The bills would have to be paid, and then there was the money she sent to her mother each week, and it would be her younger sister's birthday in less than a fortnight, and she had meant to buy her the bicycle she had been coveting. What had she done? And how would she get another job now? Not only would Dick Hunt never give her a reference, he'd go all over London telling every producer in sight that she was a bad risk, a troublemaker ...

She looked round the flat, and her eyes welled with tears of tiredness and shock. Everything in it she and Jane had chosen—rushing off to antique markets at dawn, picking things up cheap in little out-of-the-way shops. This flat *was* her independence—the first thing in her life she'd found, and paid for, and organised herself. And now, if she couldn't get another job, a well-paid job, she'd have to throw it all in ...

Impatiently, she wiped the tears away with the back of her hand. It was no good giving in to self-pity, she thought. It was her own fault. If she'd been conciliatory to Dick Hunt she could have got him to forgive her, she knew that. Then he wouldn't have fired her. But she'd have had to crawl, she thought with revulsion. She'd have had to agree to one of his intimate little dinners and heaven knows what else beside. And she couldn't have done that. But on the other hand ... why had she been so rash? She had gone rushing in, and for no better reason than that some actor she hardly knew had implied she ought to. Some actor who had—yes, made a pass at her, however much he denied it.

She wandered from room to room in a kind of blank despair. One part of her mind was adding up the bills she had to pay, another kept dragging back to the canal, to the night before, to everything that Laurence Martineau had said and done. But she tried to thrust those thoughts away. Much *he* cared, she thought bitterly. He'd gone waltzing back to his own life without so much as a second glance. He'd probably forgotten last night already . . . *Why* had she listened to him?

At about six the telephone rang again, and she snatched it up quickly, on the second ring. It was Lindy, and Kate felt her spirits, somehow momentarily raised, sink again. Lindy sounded breathless and excited.

'*What* have you been up to?' she demanded. 'What *did* you say to Dick this morning? I've been trying to phone you ever since, but he's been in the office the whole time, watching my every move. This is my first chance—I think he's gone home now to put fillet steak on his eye, or whatever you do when it's half-closed and a choice shade of blue.'

In spite of herself, Katy laughed. She curled up on the sofa beside the phone feeling a little better; Lindy was good at cheering people up—it was part of her job.

'I've resigned,' she said. 'Or been fired. Take your pick. It happened more or less simultaneously.'

'So I gather,' Lindy said drily. 'I was in the room this morning when Dick took your call, remember? I thought he was going to have apoplexy there and then. I think that was the final straw. He'd been round at his Harley Street dentist at eight, having his two front caps fixed after Mr Martineau had dislodged them, and I think he'd been working himself up nicely to the moment when he could come in here and give you a rocket—and then you robbed him of his chance! You are cruel, Katy. First you provoke our famous actor friend into propelling him into a pile of profiteroles, so he gets chocolate and cream all over his Savile Row dinner jacket, and then you rob him of his rightful revenge. It's too much. Now, do tell—did you have a good evening with Laurence Martineau? I'm too jealous for words!'

'He just drove me home from the restaurant,' said Katy, untruthfully, but without guilt. She liked Lindy, but she didn't want to discuss what had happened last night—not with anyone.

'Did he pull up in the moonlight and recite a few sonnets?'

'Sorry to disappoint you. Not so much as a limerick,' Katy said, trying to keep her tone light.

'Well, you know he's been calling you here today?' Katy could hear a slight edge in Lindy's voice, which sounded for a moment almost jealous. She caught her breath.

'Calling me? At the studio? What happened?'

'I don't know, I didn't take the call. He rang twice, I think.
Dick said to tell all callers you'd left, period, so I should think
that's what they said.'

'Didn't they give him my number here?' Katy suddenly felt
as if she could burst with frustration.

'Katy! You know we never give out anyone's number—
studio policy, dear, remember?'

'Well, did they get a number where I can ring him back?'
Katy was aware that she sounded too eager, and was angry
with herself.

'He said he couldn't leave a number, I believe. Why? Don't
you know where he's staying? I thought you would.'

This time there was an unmistakable edge in Lindy's voice,
a kind of avid curiosity that Katy didn't much like.

'No,' she said flatly, 'I don't know. Never mind. It doesn't
matter.'

Whether or not Lindy registered the slight snub, Katy didn't
know, but anyway she didn't (to her relief) press the matter.

'What are you going to do now?' she asked. 'Have you
thought about another job? It's not easy, you know. I had
half a mind to follow your example today, Dick was so foul,
but honestly, I couldn't. Metropolitan pay so well . . . Still. If
it's any help, there's a cousin of mine who's working at the
B.B.C. I could talk to him if you like. He *might* need a researcher, you never know, and he hates Dick, so your having
left would be a recommendation . . .'

Suddenly Katy felt terribly tired, and the black mood of the
afternoon descended on her again. Just now, she thought, she
didn't want to make any plans . . .

'Thank you, Lindy,' she said, 'I don't quite know what I'll
do now. I'll probably take a bit of a break and then look
around for another job. Could I call you next week, maybe?'

'Sure,' said Lindy, her voice sounding warmer. 'Do that.
But don't forget—I'm happy to have a word with him. Just let
me know, O.K.? And meanwhile, don't get into any more
tangles with famous actors—it's not your style.'

When she rang off, Katy sank back against the cushions.
That last remark had been a bit barbed, she thought, but then
Lindy was probably right. All this *wasn't* her style. She felt

hopelessly out of her depth. Just seven months ago she'd been
living at home in Suffolk, where the most exciting event of the
week was dinner at one of her sisters', or a tennis match in the
village. And a wave of homesickness swept over her. Why had
she ever come to London? she thought hopelessly. Why had
she ever believed she could cope with a job like that, with
people like Dick Hunt and . . . She should never have done it.
Why hadn't she married Bob? He'd asked her often enough.
She knew him as well as she knew her own family. As long as
she could remember, he'd always been there to turn to. He
was good and reliable and kind and gentle. He had a good job
as a junior consultant at a hospital, not a glamorous job,
maybe, but a fine one, and he'd always promised her that he
would look after her and her mother. She would never have to
worry about money again; the house in Suffolk would be safe.

She had only to say the word. The hospital where Bob
worked was half an hour away. She could ring him now. But
she didn't. Instead, her mind was drawn insidiously back to
the night before, to that shadowy towpath, and that strange
dark man who had sat beside her staring down into the water
as if . . . as if what? Almost as if he could drown something,
some memory, just by staring at that black silent water.

Thinking of the canal, she fell asleep, lying awkwardly and
uncomfortably, but sleeping deeply out of worry and exhaustion.

Something woke her, with a start, but Katy had to wrench
herself awake, and it took a moment to realise that it was the
doorbell, pealing insistently, as if someone downstairs had
been ringing for some while and had kept their finger on the
bell. Instantly she jerked herself upright, and rushed to the
door, cursing the fact that there was no answering device up
to the flat. She flung it open and raced down the stairs, and
across the hall. The bell had stopped. She struggled with the
locks and wrenched open the front door.

Bob was already retreating down the steps.

'Katy!' He turned and smiled up at her. 'I've been ringing
for ages—I'd just given up and was about to go back to the
hospital. Look. I've brought you something.'

He turned back up the steps, and thrust a bunch of flowers
into her arms. They were red roses, beautiful full flowers, not

the thin fragile kind you find in a florist's, but proper garden roses, with a rich, heavy scent.

'Oh, Bob, thank you,' Katy said, taking the flowers and burying her face in them. A wave of disappointment had flooded over her, which she couldn't explain, and she didn't want him to see it in her eyes.

'I was off duty yesterday,' he told her. 'So I went home for the day. They're from our garden. I was going to bring them round anyway, but I read the papers this morning, and then I thought I'd better come round as soon as I could. What have you been up to? Fights in West End restaurants, indeed!'

'Oh, that was nothing,' she said as lightly as she could. 'The papers exaggerate everything.'

'Do they?' He looked at her keenly, and Katy knew he knew her too well for her to be able to disguise her feelings.

'You're upset,' he said, 'aren't you? What's happened? I rang you at the studios this afternoon, and they said you'd left. Is that true?'

Katy attempted a watery smile. 'Yes,' she said, 'it's true. I've resigned. And been fired. All in one day—quite eventful, really.'

He looked at her, and then at his watch, and she knew that he wanted to stay, but that he probably had to go back to the hospital. Suddenly she found herself hoping strongly that he didn't; if only she could talk to him, she thought, the way she had so often before when things went wrong, then everything would fall into its proper perspective.

'Do you have to go?' she asked quickly. 'Why don't you come in? I can make you supper if you like. Jane's out, and there's lots of food in the fridge.'

She saw a shadow pass over his face, and he shook his head.

'Katy,' he said, 'I can't. I'm on call tonight. There's no way I can shift it . . .' He saw her face, and quickly took her hand.

'Hey,' he said gently, 'it's bad, isn't it? Whatever's happened? Things were going fine the other night when I saw you, and now all this. What have you got yourself mixed up in? If you've been having trouble with that fellow Hunt I'll . . .'

She shook her head quickly. 'No,' she said, 'it's not him. Not exactly . . .'

He heard her hesitation, and lightly tilted her chin up so she had to face him.

'Who, then?' he said sharply. 'That wretched actor you were allegedly with last night? Katy, how can you go getting mixed up with people like that?'

'No, no,' she said, 'it's nothing to do with him. I just went to that dinner at Angelo's and then came home. It's ... well, it's throwing in the job, I suppose. I ought to have done it ages ago. I ought never to have taken it, you were quite right. But still, it's a bit of a shock.'

And that was the truth, she thought defensively, as she felt the tears prick behind her eyes. It was just being without a job so suddenly that had started this feeling of black despair. It was nothing to do with Laurence Martineau himself; he was just the catalyst ...

'Look.' Bob took the roses firmly out of her hands and placed them gently on the steps. 'Come here.' And he drew her into his arms, holding her gently against the tweed of his jacket, just as he had done so many times before, ever since she was a little girl, whenever she was upset, when she was crying. 'Now listen to me,' he said gently. 'There's nothing for you to worry about, you know that. I think it's the best possible thing you've left that job. It was never right for you. But you had to find that out for yourself. You've got to decide what you want, Katy. You know how I feel. You know what *I* want, and now, maybe ...'

She heard the catch in his voice, and stiffened. He stroked her hair gently.

'It's all right,' he said. 'Don't worry, I'm not going to start proposing to you all over again. Not here and now anyway. I just can't bear to see you upset, to see you doing the wrong thing ... Listen. I can come round first thing tomorrow morning if you like. I'm off duty at six. I'll come round and you can give me breakfast, and we'll talk the whole thing over. How would that be?'

'Don't be silly.' She drew away from him gently. 'You'll have been on duty all night. When are you supposed to sleep?'

'I'll fit it in somehow,' said Bob, and smiled, the familiar, slightly crooked smile she knew so well. 'There are more important things than sleep, Katy. Though to judge from the look of you, an early night wouldn't do you any harm. Now,'

He tilted her face up to him again, so she had to meet his clear blue-eyed gaze. 'Will you be O.K. tonight? I can ring you later if you'd like me to?'

She shook her head, wordlessly.

'All right. Now I prescribe hot milk, an undemanding book, twelve hours' sleep, and bacon and eggs for me at nine o'clock tomorrow morning. No worry, and positively no late-night dinners in smart restaurants with undesirably jet-set actors. O.K.?'

He made her laugh, just as he had meant to. He was *right*, she thought, looking at his boyish, kind open face. What had she been getting tangled up with a man like Laurence Martineau, who doled out a lot of advice and lectures, caused scenes and then walked away from them? Last night, in the car outside this house, he'd been so cold, so casual ... just the way she had been to Bob sometimes in the past, when she hadn't wanted to get too involved ... She blushed at the memory, and drew Bob back to her, guilt adding to the warmth and affection that suddenly welled up in her.

'I'll do just as you say,' she said demurely. 'Doctor's orders. And I might even give you mushrooms with the bacon and eggs. It's a date.'

'Katy?'

She recognised the rough enquiry in his voice, for she rarely let him kiss her. This time she lifted her face, and he took her gently in his arms. But at the last moment something—some memory he had unknowingly stirred up—made her turn her face away. His lips brushed hers lightly. He held her close to him for a moment, then released her awkwardly. She could see a certain pain in his eyes, and hated herself for causing it. *Next time*, she promised herself silently. *Next time* I shan't be so cold to him.

'I'll have to go.' He hesitated. 'Don't forget the roses.' She shook her head and picked them up.

'Till tomorrow, then,' he said, and as she straightened up, and could see the street below them for the first time, she saw Laurence Martineau standing at the bottom of the steps. He had his hands in his pockets and was leaning against the railings, looking up with an expression of insolent amusement on his face.

Seeing her expression change, Bob swung round. There was

a short, tense silence. Katy felt the colour rush to her face. How long had he been standing there? Had he seen . . .?

Laurence Martineau broke the silence.

'Good evening,' he said smoothly. 'I'm sorry, I appear to be interrupting.'

Bob hesitated for an instant, and Katy knew that he had recognised the actor at once. He glanced from Laurence Martineau to her, then turned and went down the steps. She knew what he was thinking—that this meeting had been arranged, that she had been lying to him. His face was pale with anger, and she moved forward quickly to say something, anything, perhaps to make some ludicrous introduction, but Bob forestalled her.

'Not at all,' he said coolly to Laurence Martineau, passing straight by him. 'Goodnight, Katy. I'll see you in the morning.'

Then he was gone—typically, Katy thought. Nothing would make him late for the hospital; it was not in his nature to make scenes. She stood there at the top of the steps, clutching the roses to her white dress, staring down at the tall lounging figure of Laurence Martineau. There was a silence which seemed to her to go on for eternity. When Bob had rounded the corner and was out of sight, Laurence Martineau straightened up, and unconcernedly brushed the sleeve of his jacket, where it had been resting against a rusty railing.

'Do you have whisky in your flat?' he asked. 'I thought you might not have, so I took the precaution of bringing it with me.' He gestured towards the pocket of the jacket he was wearing. 'I'm sorry,' he added. 'I didn't think to bring flowers. A little remiss of me, but I can see that has been attended to.'

He came up the steps and stood in the doorway.

'Well?' he said. 'Are you going to invite me inside, or do I have to force an entry? You really are the most extraordinarily unwelcoming young woman.'

'What are you doing here?' Suddenly Katy found her tongue again, and she felt furiously angry. How dared he turn up here, causing more confusion and complication, and just assume that he could walk into her flat?

'What makes you think that you can simply turn up on someone's doorstep, and march into their house? You really are the most high-handed man I've ever . . .'

'Shall we discuss it inside?' He held the door open for her. 'It's beginning to get cold, you're wearing a thin dress, and you've already been standing about on the doorstep for some time.'

'That's my affair,' she said hotly. 'I don't know what you think gives you the right just to . . .'

'Do come inside and stop arguing,' he said coolly. 'It's extremely tiresome. I want to talk to you. The studio refused to give me your telephone number, so in the circumstances, there was nothing else I could do but come round. Do you agree?'

'Well, yes,' she said reluctantly. 'But I think we can perfectly well say anything we have to say to each other here, don't you?'

'No,' he said, 'I don't. Otherwise I wouldn't have come. Now, come inside.'

He caught her by the wrist and pulled her sharply inside the door, slamming it shut. They both stood, close to each other, in the dark hall, their breath coming quickly, and for a moment Katy thought he was going to pull her into his arms again, just as he had the night before. But he released her with a polite and infuriating smile.

'Now,' he said, 'would you mind showing me where your flat is, or are you going to continue to be ill-tempered and inhospitable?'

'Very well,' she said angrily. 'Since you leave me no option, and I know your talent for causing scenes. It's on the third floor, and there's no lift.'

'Thank you.' He made an elaborate gesture towards the stairs, and Katy pushed past him and went up ahead, her mind in a whirl.

When they reached the door to her flat, Katy went inside ahead of him and turned on the lamps in the sitting room, so that it was suffused with a soft light. He followed her nonchalantly, came into the room, and stationed himself by the fireplace, leaning on the mantelpiece, and looked down at her unsmilingly.

She sat down on one of the sofas, and tried to look unconcerned and unaffected, as if she had not given him a second thought since the previous evening, and it was the most natural thing in the world for her to be receiving a world-famous actor, alone in her apartment. She found herself wondering moment-

arily how the room looked to him, whether it looked shabby—
he must be used to such grand houses—and also how she
looked herself. Thank goodness she had taken such trouble in
dressing that day, she thought. Supposed he had turned up
and she had been wearing her oldest clothes . . . She smoothed
down the skirt of her white dress, intensely conscious of his
gaze upon her.

'Who was that young man?' he asked finally, in a peremp-
tory manner.

'A friend.'

'An old friend?'

Katy felt herself bristling. 'I don't really see that it's any of
your business,' she said, 'but since you ask, yes, a very old
friend.'

'I see.' The words were said coldly, and he moved away, so
his back was towards her, looking out of the windows at the
gardens below. 'Then don't you think you ought to put his
flowers in water? They'll wilt. They are Roserie de la Haie,
unless I'm mistaken, which is rather a rare rose. It could be a
pity to spoil them, particularly since they're a gift from such
an old friend.'

Katy ignored the sarcasm in his voice. At least arranging
the flowers gave her something to do. She took the roses into
the kitchen, ran some water, and filled an old pitcher. Then
she stood the roses in it, arranging them very casually, and
taking her time. She half expected him to follow her, but he
did not—to her irritation—and finally she was forced to go
back, carrying the flowers.

He gave her an ironic smile as she came back.

'Very beautiful,' he said, gesturing to the roses, but looking
at her face. She put the flowers on an old polished table near
the window, then went and stood awkwardly by the fireplace.

Laurence Martineau had settled himself in the sofa opposite
her, leaning back on the cushions, and looking composedly
around the room.

He was wearing more casual clothes than he had had on the
previous day, and for a moment Katy wondered where he had
been the night before, and earlier that day. He had brought
no luggage with him; did he still keep a house in London, and
had he changed his clothes there? Or did he perhaps stay with
this woman he was planning to marry? Did she live in London,

and if so, where was she this evening? His clothes were casual, but beautifully cut: narrow camel-coloured corduroy trousers, deeply polished boots, a cream silk shirt open at the neck, and a loose linen jacket in beige. His long legs were crossed and Katy noticed, irritably, for she felt acutely selfconscious, that he looked perfectly at ease.

'Can you light a fire in this fireplace?' he asked.

'Yes,' she said, surprised by the question. 'You're not supposed to burn wood, but we do sometimes—there are some logs and some special smokeless briquette things in the kitchen. Why?'

'Because it might look pretty—it might warm you up, get rid of that pallor. I don't know, I like them. Here—sit down. I'll bring you a drink and light a fire.'

He got up, settled her on the sofa opposite him, as if she were an invalid, found glasses, and poured her some Scotch. He disappeared into the kitchen and returned with some firewood, and Katy sat there, sipping her drink in a daze, wondering what on earth was happening to her.

'Do you always behave like this in someone else's house?' she asked finally, as he arranged logs and coals with some expertise, and then set a match to them.

'How do you mean?' He knelt back on his heels and looked at her quizzically.

'Well, do you normally walk into people's houses and tell them to sit down, fetch them drinks, and then start lighting fires?'

He smiled. 'No, normally I suppose I don't, but you look as if you might need a little organisation at the moment. You look slightly wan. Warmth and whisky will do you good, and why should you have to be the one to provide it? Why? Do you object? You really are an extremely quarrelsome young woman.'

'No, I don't object. Do make yourself at home.'

He ignored the ironic inflection. 'Thank you,' he said. 'I shall.'

He fetched himself a Scotch, and sat down opposite her. The fire blazed with a quick heat, warming the room, and sending flickering red shadows on the walls and rugs.

'Very good,' he commented, stretching out his legs to the warmth. 'Much better. Now tell me, do you live here alone?'

'No.'

'Am I to play a tiresome guessing game to find out who you live here with, or are you going to tell me?'

'Why do you want to know?'

'Because I would like to know a little bit more about you,' he said, unsmilingly. 'Is that a crime? So, tell me. Is it a maiden aunt? I think not. Some earnest flatmates with spectacles, who tell you what they read in the library that afternoon, and reveal the yearnings of their hearts—in confidence, of course—over the midnight Ovaltine? Or is it a young man—or possibly even an older man—with whom you live in metropolitan extra-marital bliss?'

'I share this flat with one other girl,' Katy answered, as crisply as she could. 'She doesn't wear spectacles, or spend much time in libraries, and if you check the cupboards, which you probably have done already, you'll find we don't drink Ovaltine. Does that answer your question?'

'Partly,' he said, looking at her intently. 'Not entirely. But then, as you quite rightly say, I really have little right to ask.'

He had registered the snub in her voice, Katy knew instantly, and she wasn't sure if she were glad or sorry. At least, she thought wryly, she had regained a little of the initiative. Laurence Martineau seemed to have a gift for taking command of situations, for forcing the pace, and it left her feeling awkward and desperately unsure of her ground. He, on the other hand, seemed incapable of being embarrassed or other than perfectly at ease. She looked at him covertly now, as he sat there, looking as if his presence were the most natural thing in the world, and required no explanation whatsoever. Why had he come? she thought desperately to herself. What did he want now, and why was he asking so many questions? Probably he just wanted to find out what had happened to her at work, she told herself quickly. Maybe he felt a little guilty at the turn that events had taken the night before. Anyway, it was nothing to get in a state about. No doubt he would leave just as suddenly as he had arrived, and go off to dinner—perhaps with one of those women whose name had been linked with his in the gossip columns that morning, perhaps with someone else, with whoever the mystery woman was he had mentioned so slyly and so charmingly in Dick Hunt's interview. Yet his presence disturbed Katy deeply, just as it had the previous day, and she had to fight to shake off the nervousness, even the elation, which gripped her. No doubt it was because she had admired him so much on stage in the past, she thought crossly to herself. Well, she had no intention of being infatuated with a famous film star, still less of letting him imagine for one second that she was . . .

'You read the papers this morning?' he asked suddenly.

'Some of them,' she said, casually and untruthfully. 'Yes.'

'The usual lies,' he said flatly. 'I told you, Dick Hunt must have enjoyed talking to them.'

His earlier lightness seemed to have left him suddenly, and he was staring into the fire with that same tired resignation she had glimpsed the night before. He looked so unhappy, she thought, and she wondered why—this man, who seemed to have everything anyone could want.

'You dislodged some of his precious capped teeth, you know,' she told him lightly, trying, in spite of herself, to raise his spirits. 'He was round at his dentist at the crack of dawn this morning.'

'Did I?' Some animation returned to his face, and he smiled. 'I suppose I should feel guilty. Actually, that's the first good piece of news I've heard today.' He glanced across at her and the wicked amusement in his eyes made her laugh too. The laughter eased some of the tension in the room, and Katy felt better. That was the right tactic, she thought; if only she could keep the conversation light, and normal—just until he made a move to go.

As she thought it, he rose to his feet, and with a lurch of feeling she thought he *was* going, but he merely fetched her another drink. He gave it to her, then lingered by her side, so she dropped her eyes.

'Well now,' he said. 'Perhaps you'd better tell me why you've left your job.'

It was a statement, not a question, and Katy knew it would be useless to try and evade it. 'I resigned this morning,' she said levelly, 'and was fired simultaneously. That's all.'

'And why did you resign?'

He seated himself on the arm of the sofa and looked down unwaveringly into her face.

'Oh, I don't know,' she said quickly. 'For some time I'd felt

. . . that it wasn't the right job for me. And other people were
against it . . .'

'Other people?'

'Oh yes,' she said hurriedly. 'My mother, for one, and—
well, some of my friends, so . . .'

'So what I said last night had nothing to do with it?'

She hesitated. If she said too much it would look as though
she were trying to shoulder him with the responsibility for her
resignation, and anyway, she thought, it wasn't really due to
him. It had been the scene at dinner, Dick Hunt's disgusting
insinuations . . .

She cleared her throat, and tried to control the rising nervousness that his closeness started up in her. A little of her
whisky spilled on to her dress.

. 'What you said just crystallised certain things, that's all,'
she said stiffly. 'I had thought I ought to resign before, and
anyway it's all immaterial, because Dick fired me. He just did
it over the phone instead of face to face.'

'How disappointing for him,' he said, and again she heard
that savage dislike in his voice that she had heard before, just
before he had hit Hunt. 'So,' he went on without a note of
sympathy in his voice, 'what are you going to do now? Are
you going to take up one of the other options you outlined to
me yesterday?'

For a moment she wondered what he meant, and then
realised he must be referring to what she had said about marriage, about settling down. Her cheeks flamed with colour.

'I don't know,' she muttered. 'I haven't really had time to
think about it.'

'I see,' he said coldly. His eyes strayed across the room to
the red roses on the table, and she realised what he was thinking. Well, let him, she said to herself angrily. The man didn't
have a shred of human feeling or sympathy in him; how different he was from Bob—and yet Bob didn't make her hand
shake when he sat next to her.

'Well, you're very young,' he said flatly, as if that was all
there was to be said in the matter. He got up and moved
away, pacing up and down the room for a few moments. His
dismissiveness stung her.

'Not that young,' she said tartly. 'I'm twenty-three. I'm old
enough to know my own mind.'

'I thought that when I was twenty-eight,' he said tersely, 'when I'd seen a good deal more of the world than you have. I'm thirty-eight now, which must seem as old as the hills to you. It certainly sounds a long way from twenty-three anyway. With the wisdom of my age I would doubt very much if you do know your own mind, but I don't expect you to listen to me.'

He had lost his air of coolness, and looked almost agitated, Katy thought. She tried desperately to remember what had happened to him when he was twenty-eight which now made him sound so bitter. But her memory for dates was poor, and she couldn't remember. She looked at the troubled face and the dark, mysterious eyes, and felt her heart catch—*why* was he so unhappy? For the first time that evening she stopped fighting the feelings that his nearness awoke in her, and spoke to him directly, with no sharpness or coldness in her voice.

'I don't see why you should say that,' she said quietly, looking directly at him. 'I would listen to you. Of course I would.'

'Would you?' he said, almost angrily, turning back, and standing glowering down at her. 'You don't know what you're talking about. Why should you listen to me? I've just helped you to lose your job, got your name plastered across those cheap newspapers . . . and anyway . . .' He turned away again, so she could not see his face. 'I've mismanaged my own life, God knows! Why should I tell anyone how to manage theirs?'

'I don't see that you've mismanaged your life,' she said indignantly. 'You're a fine actor, a great actor . . .'

'A film actor!' He laughed, but there was no amusement in the sound. 'Bankable in Hollywood terms, so they tell me. Three months a year, twice a year, on location, filming some god-awful rubbish put together by a team of semi-literates. An agent, a manager, an accountant. A happy bank manager. An even happier man at the Inland Revenue. A million dollars a picture, and keep up with the alimony payments. Oh yes! A fine actor!'

'You don't have to make those films,' she said hotly. 'I can't think why you do. You could go back to the stage whenever you wanted.'

'Could I?' he said fiercely, turning and glaring at her. 'Could I? How easy you make it all sound, with the wisdom of your twenty-three years. You don't know what you're talking about.'

'Yes, I do,' she said angrily, standing up, and facing him. 'No one needs to be paid the kind of salary you get for those stupid films you've been making. You could earn enough money in the theatre easily, there's no problem—the best companies want you, the parts are there waiting for you to play them . . .'

They were facing each other now, only a few feet between them, and his face was dark with anger. The expression on it frightened her, it was so fierce and so embittered. Katy didn't know where she had found the courage to speak like that— perhaps from the whisky, perhaps from out of the tension of that long bleak day, but mainly from a sudden impetuous desire to say to him what she passionately felt. After all, he would soon be gone, he would be back in France. She would never see him again, so why not say what she believed?

For one strange moment she almost thought he was going to hit her. But suddenly the anger went from his face as swiftly as it had come. It was replaced with an insolent mocking stare, which did not quite erase the hurt in his eyes. He was *acting*, she thought incredulously.

'What touching concern,' he said flippantly. 'I really am almost overwhelmed that you should have considered the matter. Finance, I must tell you, my dear, doesn't really enter into it, so you're wrong there. Now, shall we change the subject? This is all terribly boring, I'm afraid.'

'Why is it boring?' Katy demanded fiercely. 'You don't mean that! You didn't sound bored a minute ago. You sounded angry and bitter—why pretend?'

'Do stop lecturing me,' he sighed, keeping the flippant tone of voice. 'Let me get you a last drink. This is all getting rather silly and juvenile. I didn't come here tonight, my dear, to be told what do do with my life.'

'Don't patronise me!' Katy almost shouted at him. 'And don't call my "my dear" in that horrible, affected insincere way . . . it's hateful!'

The mocking expression disappeared from his face as quickly as it had come. He moved towards her suddenly, with the swift movement that characterised him; his dark eyes searched hers for a few moments, then seemed to be satisfied by what he saw there.

'Kate,' he said, and his voice sounded roughened, tight with emotion, 'are you being honest with me? I think you are, but I'm not sure.'

She was shaking, and she knew he must sense it, they were standing so close. Desperately she tried to control her own voice, and the feeling of attraction which was, insidiously, beginning to pulse again in every vein of her body. 'I've said what I think,' she said quietly, lowering her eyes from that harsh gaze. 'I probably had no business to . . . I'm interfering, and I don't understand . . . I'm sorry.'

He didn't answer her, but stood quite still looking down at her. She realised she wanted to touch him, to take his hand, to make some gesture—of what she wasn't quite sure. Comfort perhaps, for that look of pain was etched again on his features. But she didn't dare, and the moment passed. When he spoke again his voice was quiet, and his face gentle.

'You look very tired,' he said. 'I probably shouldn't have come here, and I certainly shouldn't have started talking about . . . about all that. You should go to bed, and get some sleep.'

'It's all right,' she said, suddenly afraid, now that he was leaving, and feeling that great void would open up again. 'I don't want you to go.'

'I think I'd better,' he said, and the half-mocking smile reappeared. 'I don't think a young lady should encourage a rakish actor to stay at this time of night, do you? Particularly a young lady with your prospects.'

What prospects? Katy was about to ask him bitterly, but he forestalled her. He moved away, and when he spoke again, his voice had become cool again, and impersonal.

'I did come here with a purpose, as a matter of fact,' he told her. 'But you probably won't be interested in what I was going to suggest, given your plans, and everything.'

'What plans?' Katy said desperately. 'I have no real plans, I told you, I haven't had time to think . . .'

She saw his eyes glance at the roses again, and he seemed to hesitate for a moment.

'Would you be interested in a job?' he said finally, almost offhandedly. 'It's only a temporary job, for a few months— but maybe you would be interested in something for a short while, just until . . . well, until you've decided exactly what you are going to do next, and when.'

'A job?' She didn't know what she had expected him to say, but it wasn't that.

'Yes,' he said, and he was already moving towards the door. 'It's not really suited to your capabilities, but it might be quite pleasant, and it's only for a short while.'

'What is it?'

'Well, I don't really think you'd like it,' he said, sounding suddenly embarrassed. 'It's just that my present secretary is getting married, and she'll be away for a few months, probably three, or four at the outside. I shall need someone in France while she's away, and of course, I haven't got round to organising it. It's awfully boring, I'm afraid, just dealing with fan letters mainly, and keeping my affairs in order, because I'm very bad at it myself. But it's in Provence, which is lovely at this time of year, and it's not particularly arduous . . .'

'I see,' she said.

'I'm not asking you because I feel guilty about your losing your job, or about what I said last night—please don't think that. And I realise, of course, that you probably want something more testing. Or anyway, you'll want to be in England, with your . . . friends, and so on. I'm sorry. It was a silly suggestion. Forget it—I just thought . . .'

'No,' she said, her mind whirling, 'I don't have to be in England, and anyway, if it's only for a short while . . .'

'It can be for just a month, if you like,' he said quickly. 'It would help me enormously, and I could probably manage quite well after that until my secretary comes back . . .'

They stared at each other across the room, both awkward and selfconscious now. Katy thought she knew why he was making this offer, for all that he said. He probably did feel sorry for her, she thought, and perhaps a little guilty that, after his remarks last night, there she was, unemployed, and quite likely to remain so. But his charity didn't rankle, and she felt her heart lift. Of course, she thought quickly, it would be lovely to go to Provence, and it would give her breathing space until she could look for another job in London. She'd be able to pay the bills, send her mother some money, buy the bicycle for her sister . . . A huge sense of relief flooded over her. Actually, it felt more like happiness, but she told herself it was relief.

'When would you need to know?' she said, forcing herself

to sound businesslike.

'Well, I'm going back to France the day after tomorrow. Then, if it's not too soon.'

'I'll let you know tomorrow,' she said. 'Would you like me to ring?'

They both sounded ridiculously stilted and silly, she thought, particularly in contrast to the way they had been speaking earlier. Perhaps he felt it too, because he obviously decided to curtail the matter, almost as if he regretted the decision.

'Tell me your telephone number,' he said. 'I'll phone you tomorrow. If you want, we can talk in more detail then. I'd offer the same salary you were paid at Metropolitan, of course.'

'Ring me tomorrow afternoon,' she said, more calmly than she felt, and gave him the number. 'Do you need something to write it down?'

He shook his head. 'It's engraved on my mind. I'll ring tomorrow at four.'

He took her hand briefly. 'Goodnight,' he said, 'I'll let myself out.'

And before she could say anything else, he had opened the door, closed it behind him, and was gone.

CHAPTER FIVE

As soon as the plane crossed the Channel, the cloud lifted; perhaps it was an omen, Katy thought. What was that line? *Set fair for France* ... Below the plane now she could see folds of green and gold, bathed in brilliant light. But they were still too high to make out any features. She looked at her watch; another half hour at least before they began their descent. She sipped the orange juice the stewardess had brought her, and wondered momentarily if maybe she would have been wiser to have something stronger, just to soothe her nerves. She sighed and brushed the thick hair back from her face; no, that was nonsense. She felt nervous, yes, but there really was no need. It was just that everything seemed to have happened so fast. Eight days ago she had never met Laurence Martineau; seven days ago she had been driving out to Heathrow in that Daimler; six days ago he had turned up at her flat; five, and she had agreed to come to Provence ...

It hadn't been the easiest of decisions, she thought. In fact, if she hadn't been in such a desperate mood about money, about getting another job, she probably would never have agreed. After all, practically everyone else had told her she was mad, that she was making completely the wrong decision. Her mother had been upset, of course, and then Bob ...

The thought of Bob made her feel guilty, and she shifted in her seat. He had come round for breakfast as arranged, and she hadn't told him what had happened, not at first anyway. But he had questioned her so closely that in the end she had, and then—well, then he had been so hurt and so angry and so uncomprehending that she had practically decided there and then that the trip to Provence was out of the question. Yet when Laurence Martineau had rung, she'd said yes, surprising even herself, without any hesitation, as if she had already made up her mind. And then, she thought wryly, then it had gone from bad to worse. Bob had come round to the flat the same evening, when Jane was there, and they had sat and argued and argued, round and round in circles . . .

Jane had sat idly on the sofa, twisting her strawberry-coloured curls round her fingers, smoking endless cigarettes, and saying practically nothing. Then, when Bob had said for the umpteenth time, 'Well, I can't think why Katy wants to go, it's a rotten job anyway', suddenly Jane had stood up and stretched. 'I must say I think you're both being colossally boring,' she had said. 'It's perfectly obvious why he offered her the job, and why she's taking it. I should think they fancy each other. And what's wrong with that? Good luck, I say. Send us a postcard, Katy love. Now I'm going to bed.'

With which line she had made an effective exit, leaving (no doubt as she had intended) a stormy silence behind her.

'Is that true, Katy?' Bob asked in a quiet, even voice.

'No, certainly not. It's absolute rubbish. Typical of Jane.'

'Well, I hope you know what you're letting yourself in for, that's all.' Bob had looked angrier than she had ever seen him. 'He looked like a typical actor to me . . .'

'And what's a typical actor supposed to look like?' she had snapped.

'Conceited and arrogant, if you want to know. Thoroughly unreliable. Maybe a bit of a rake as well, Katy. You know what they say about actors' morals . . .'

It had been the last straw. Katy had flounced out. Had she never noticed how smug Bob could be? she had thought.

Still, she couldn't get the scene out of her mind. It flooded back to her now as the plane wheeled, and the instruction to fasten seat-belts for the landing suddenly flashed on above her seat. There was no truth in what Jane had said, of course. She'd convinced Bob of that by the time she left. He had come to see her off, and the atmosphere had been tense, but better then. She would write, she thought. Lots of letters. The time in France was just what she needed to sort herself out, and Bob seemed resigned to that now. And then, when she came back—and she wouldn't stay long, probably a month at most—well, then perhaps everything would be clearer. Perhaps she and Bob could make a new beginning.

She began to gather up her hand luggage, feeling more in control than she had for days. After all, she was here to work. It was stupid to have worried about what Jane had said, stupid to have let that memory of a harsh, angry kiss by the canal

dwell in her thoughts. What you have to think about now, she
told herself crossly, is whether your typing is going to be up to
scratch. After all, she wasn't fifteen any more, and she had no
illusions as to why she had been asked to come here.

The plane banked, hovered, then landed smoothly. The airport at Toulon was quite small, she saw, as she peered curiously from the window. When she walked down the airplane
steps and on to the tarmac, the heat hit her. It was brilliantly
sunny, and the clear, hard light bounced back off the white
walls of the airport building. Katy walked inside, found her
cases, passed through Customs. All around her were crowds
of French families, hugging and kissing, ebbing back and
forth. She looked anxiously around her. Laurence Martineau
had said he would meet the flight, but there was no sign of
him anywhere. She pushed her way through into the outer
lobby, past the car rental desks, past the small café, then
suddenly she saw him.

He was standing leaning against the wall by the glass doors
out of the airport. A tall, thin figure, dressed in white, which
accentuated the tanned skin, the thick black hair. He had that
same quality of poise, of complete stillness, as when she had
first seen him. Amidst the bustle and hubbub of the airport he
stood alone, detached, a spectator, utterly uninvolved. As she
saw him, the noise and movement seemed wiped out. For a
moment there was only this man, the space between them, and
a great silence.

'Katharine,' he said, and came forward and took her hand
warmly. The room righted itself, and the noise resumed.

'I have the car outside. Let's get away from all this confusion. We'll be back at La Bayardière in twenty minutes, and
there's some good white wine in the fridge. You must be exhausted.'

He picked up her cases and ushered her outside. His car
was parked—illegally—immediately outside the doors. It was
a beautiful old Lagonda, cream and black, with a landau roof,
which was down. He deposited Katy and her bags inside, and
then accelerated swiftly away.

'Are you feeling all right? You look a bit pale.'

She smiled. 'I'm fine. It was just the sudden heat, I think.
I'm O.K. now. This is lovely.'

'You don't mind the top being down?' He glanced mischievously at her, then back to the road. 'It plays havoc with the hair.'

'I don't mind,' she said, and she had to shout, for the slipstream carried her words away.

'Good flight?'

She nodded.

'You're in luck,' he said, 'the weather's holding. It's been incredibly hot—it's still like summer. Oh——' he gestured at the back seat, 'I brought you a present.'

She turned, and there on the narrow back seat was an enormous bunch of lavender, tied with blue silk ribbon.

'From the hills round the house. I picked it this morning. That and rosemary—the scent of Provence.'

She picked up the bouquet, and was instantly enveloped in the heady perfume from the flowers.

'It's beautiful!' she shouted.

'Not roses,' he said. 'Still.'

They had been speeding along the motorway which went from the airport to Toulon and then on along the coast towards Nice and Cannes, but shortly he turned off the road, slowed down, and urged the car expertly along a narrow winding road that led up into the hills. Katy looked around, and caught her breath at the beauty of it. White dust spun up from the wheels behind them. On either side of the tiny road were fields of vines and fig trees. The hills lay before them, high, with deep folds, a deep red-gold in the sunlight with terraces on their lower slopes, just rocks and tall dark narrow cypress trees above.

'It looks like the landscapes in Italian paintings,' she said. 'It's beautiful.'

'It's very like that—like Tuscany,' he said. 'But don't look too much now. I want you to look properly for the first time when we reach La Bayardière.'

The road wound on upwards, passing a few farmhouses with red-tiled roofs, peeling yellow walls, ochre shutters. Chickens pecked at the road side, and a farmer raised his hand in a brief salute. They turned off again on to an even narrower road, and an even steeper incline. Great banks of rosemary and lavender brushed the sides of the car, and the sun beat down hotly on their heads.

Katy strained her eyes, peering ahead, but the road wound

too often, and she could see no sign of the house.

Suddenly they turned a steep corner on the edge of the hillside, the car's wheels skirting a sheer drop of hundreds of feet to the valley below. In front of them was a high ochre wall, with huge iron gates which stood open. They drove through and into a wide courtyard, and Laurence Martineau pulled up.

The courtyard was paved in rough stone, surrounded with high walls, two of which seemed to be built right into the hillside. On their right was a large farmhouse, with tall windows heavily shuttered against the sun. Vines and a deep mauve plumbago grew in profusion up the front of it, and at the side was a large pergola, with a table and chairs beneath it, several cats, large numbers of chickens. On the left Katy could see a staircase that wound up above the walls and round the side of the hill. Above it she could see the tall walls, the roofs of another house, but it was facing away from the courtyard, out over the valley, so that one could not see it and just had an impression of height and size.

'Come inside.' Laurence Martineau came round and helped her out of the car. 'Gaston will bring your bags up later.'

As they approached the steps, there came a great clattering and banging from the farmhouse behind them. Katy glimpsed three small faces peering curiously from the windows, then a small, dark woman emerged from the house shooing chickens away from the door.

She waved energetically, '*Bonjour*, Monsieur Martineau,' she called.

Laurence waved back. '*Bonjour*, Marie-Christine, *voici* Mademoiselle Sutcliffe, *elle est arrivée*.'

'*Bonjour, mademoiselle*,' the little woman shrieked gaily. '*Bonjour et bienvenue!*'

Katy managed a wave and a '*Bonjour, madame*', and Laurence Martineau ushered her up the steps.

'My housekeeper,' he said, 'her family have lived here for generations. Gaston is her husband. They have three children who can't wait to meet the English *mademoiselle*. Marie-Christine cooks for me, and helps clean . . .'

They reached the top of the steps, turned along a narrow terrace high on the walls above the courtyard, rounded the corner, and Katy had her first view of La Bayardière.

It was a long, low house, of two storeys, painted a deep

umber, the colour of the earth all around them. Behind it, the
hill rose steeply to a crest some fifty feet above. At the far end
was a tower, twice as high as the house, topped with tiny
stone niches for pigeons. The roofs were terracotta tiles, deep
orange in the sunlight, and the great ranks of windows along
the face of the house looked out over the wide valley and the
hills beyond. In front of the house was a paved terrace, the
boundaries marked by the tall black columns of cypress trees;
there were flowerbeds spilling an abundance of flowers and
herbs, and roses, jasmine and plumbago grew up the walls,
cascading around the windows and the great wide door. There
was absolute stillness and quiet, the only sound the breeze
rustling the branches of the creepers, and the scratching noise
of cicadas which came from the hillside.

Laurence Martineau stood by her side, watching her face
for her reaction. He wasn't disappointed, Katy thought, for
no one could have failed to look joyful, peaceful, on seeing
such a place.

'You like it?' he asked, and the question seemed to carry
more than casual weight.

'I think it's the most beautiful house I've ever seen in my
life,' she said quickly.

He smiled. 'I'm glad. You're not sorry you came, then? I
thought you might regret it. We're very isolated here and . . .
some people . . .' he hesitated slightly, and Katy knew instantly
he meant his last wife. 'Some people find it too remote. The
nearest village is five kilometres, and here there's only Gaston,
and Marie-Christine and the children.'

'It's a perfect retreat,' she said, a little awkwardly, embarrassed by the obvious reference to Camilla Drew. A shadow
passed across his face.

'A retreat? Well, yes, I suppose it is that for me, in a sense.
But it shouldn't be really, you know. It was very much a family
house once; I remember coming here when I was a child, to
visit my uncle, and it was filled with families—aunts and
cousins and friends and hosts of children. Children love it
here—it's a perfect house for them—lots of secret places to
explore, old attics to discover. Still, that was all a long time
ago. We shall be alone here—I hope you won't find that
boring?' Without waiting for an answer, he took her arm and
led her inside.

A large tortoiseshell cat and four tiny kittens were sunning themselves on the doorstep, and they stepped over them into a cool shuttered hall. Katy just had a fleeting impression of a stone floor, white walls, some beautiful paintings, and an old walnut armoire. Laurence Martineau gestured at two doors, heavy oak, with old brass handles brilliantly polished.

'To the right is the dining room and the kitchens—though we eat outdoors mostly when the weather is like this. To the left there's my study, the drawing room, a couple of other rooms. I'll show you those later. I expect you'd like to go upstairs. I'll show you your room, and then, when you're ready, come down, and we'll have that glass of wine, and some lunch.'

He took her up a wide staircase, with uneven oak treads, that led up to a narrow landing, with an arched ceiling.

'I don't use a lot of the rooms at the moment, there's no need. Those at the back of the house are all closed up now. My room is here, and you're along at the end of the corridor.'

They passed a couple more doors, and Katy longed to open them and see the other rooms, but at the end of the corridor, as it branched off towards the back of the house, Laurence opened a door set in a stone archway, and ushered her inside.

It was a great square room, with a wooden floor and plain white walls. Two windows, with louvred shutters, ran from floor to ceiling, looped with heavy curtains of old brocade embroidered with pale roses, and faded by the sun. On one wall was a huge armoire, carved with oak leaves and pineapples, and on the other, a deep fireplace, with a marble mantel, above which hung a beautiful painting of a young woman, with long dark hair tied back at the neck.

'My mother,' he said, gesturing at the painting. 'Tchelichev painted it in Paris just before she was married. She spent her honeymoon here in this room—that armoire is an old Provençal wedding gift, traditional for brides—the oak leaves and pineapples signify fertility. Or so I'm told.'

Katy looked around her, delighted, in the cool dim air that filtered through the shutters. There was little furniture—just a heavy chest, a round table with some books, and an enormous fourposter bed, with slender carved pillars and a crocheted white coverlet. Two huge square pillows rested at the head, covered with cases of linen and lace.

'Your bathroom is through there,' Laurence Martineau
gestured at a door in the far corner. 'I hope you'll have everything you need.'

'Oh, I will!' she said, turning to him impulsively. 'Thank
you—it's all so lovely, I can't believe it. It's like a fairytale!'

He smiled, and made a gesture as if he was about to touch
her, then drew back.

'I'm glad you're pleased. We'll take things easy today, then
we can begin work in the morning, when you're rested.'

He turned and left her alone. Katy explored the room,
noting the jug of roses beside the bed, the muslin bags of
lavender in the armoire and the chest. Next door the bathroom
turned out to be inside the tower. The floor was marble, the
bath on huge claw feet, the largest she had ever seen. There
were piles of soft white towels, delicately scented soap, a long
looking-glass. She washed quickly, for she was dusty and hot,
splashed herself with some cooling cologne, and changed into
a pair of thin leather sandals she had brought in her airline
bag. She looked at herself in the glass, brushing her thick hair
loosely over her shoulders. She had bought a new dress for
the journey, and several other new dresses were in her suitcase,
which would not please her bank manager, she thought wryly,
but pleased her. The dress she was wearing was cotton, a deep
aquamarine blue. It had a tiny jacket, which she slipped off,
and underneath a small strappy top—a sundress really. The
tan she had acquired that summer in her mother's garden had
still not quite faded, she thought, and the blue of the dress
went well with the deep chestnut of her hair. She peered at her
face—wishing as usual that she hadn't so many freckles—and
put on a little lipstick. She felt nervous, a little too exposed in
the thin dress, and her hands were shaking slightly as she went
downstairs. Laurence Martineau was waiting for her on the
terrace, and he took her round to the side of the house, near
the tower, where there was a vine pergola, and under it a table
covered with a plain white cloth.

He seated her in a deep cushioned wicker chair, and poured
her a tall glass of a light greenish wine. As he handed it to
her, she saw his eyes travel over her, from sandals to face. She
wished she wasn't so thin, and then told herself not to be vain.
His eyes met hers, and for a moment she thought she saw

recognisable admiration there, but he said nothing, and turned away to pour himself wine.

'I hope your stay here will be a happy one,' he said, lifting his glass.

'I hope I shall be a good secretary,' she said, laughing.

'You were a good researcher,' he said. 'Why not?'

They sat in the shade, sipping the wine, and looking out across the valley, and Katy was very conscious all the time that, although he spoke little, his eyes never left her face. After a while, Marie-Christine arrived, chattering away in French. She brought them a great salad of olives and tomatoes, then fresh sardines from the coast grilled in vine leaves, then cheeses and a basket of fruit—peaches and nectarines, cherries and pears. They finished the first bottle of wine, and began on the second, and Katy felt lulled by the wine and the sun and the food into a somewhat sleepy peace. London seemed far away; she couldn't believe, now, that she had hesitated for a moment about coming here.

'Do you like riding?' She was suddenly aware she had been asked a question, and roused herself from her reverie.

'Yes, I do, very much.'

'Well, we can ride sometimes, if you would like it, and there are some lovely beaches very close, where nobody goes. And we can go to the market. Toulon has one of the best markets in France.'

'But I came to work,' she said, rousing herself and feeling guilty. 'You mustn't feel that you have to find things for me to do.'

'Life would be very dull,' he said, 'if one worked all the time, don't you think, Kate?'

She smiled. 'You are odd,' she said. 'Why do you call me Kate? No one else does.'

'All the more reason,' he said. 'Besides, it suits you—especially when you lose your temper, and your eyes flash and your brow wrinkles up in the most disagreeable, fierce way.'

She laughed. 'Oh dear, is it very disagreeable?'

'Very. Possibly a little spoilt too. And it does remind me of the Shrew—another woman who required a little taming.'

'I think that Kate was extremely weak,' she pronounced, a little crossly. Was she really spoilt? 'If she had had an ounce of self-respect, she would never have agreed to marry that braggart Petruchio, let alone make that awful speech she makes at the end, when she promises to obey him and everything.'

He smiled. 'Most women seem to feel that now,' he said. 'It's odd how fashions change. Fifty years ago it was thought an admirable speech—a generous one. After all, if you love someone you don't make conditions, do you? You do it totally, surely? Kate is just acknowledging that Petruchio is more important to her than her pride. They've both learned a great deal in the course of the play, after all.'

'I don't see that *he* has learned very much,' Katy said argumentatively. 'He just wants to demonstrate the hold he has over her. I don't see that love gives him the right to dominate her, humiliate her in that way.'

'No, it doesn't,' he said quietly. 'But maybe the scene is about more than a contest between them—maybe Petruchio needs some sign from her, some acknowledgement of her love. Men do need that, you know, Katharine.'

'Do they?' she said, avoiding his gaze. She felt out of her depth, suddenly young and foolish and unsure of her argument. And still cross at being called spoiled. 'And what acknowledgement does he give her in return?'

'What a legal mind you have,' he commented. 'He is marrying her, after all.'

'And that's enough?'

He looked away, as if suddenly bored. 'It ought to be a beginning,' he said slowly. 'But perhaps you're right, it's not enough.'

There was a moment's silence, and again she had the sensation that some gulf had opened up between them. She had said the wrong thing, perhaps, anyway his mind had wandered away, and she had the sensation that he was thinking about something she did not know of, did not understand. The peace and tranquillity had evaporated, and she again felt nervous and on edge.

Laurence sensed the change in mood too, because he rose suddenly to his feet, interrupting the conversation.

'Well,' he said, and his voice sounded formal and distant once more, 'I have some work to do this afternoon. May I leave you to rest? Do wander around and explore if you'd like to. The terrace is the best place if you wanted to sit out in the

sun, but be careful—it's really very hot. If you need any books
there are masses in my study. I'll see you later this evening.
Have a pleasant afternoon.'

He nodded in her direction, and left abruptly.

Katy felt embarrassed and stupid. She should not have
begun that argument, she thought, and she had drunk too
much wine at lunch. Obviously she had said something which
brought back memories of his marriage, and again, she had
been brusque, impolite. She felt angry with herself, and unhappy, and wondered how she should spend the afternoon.
She sat on the terrace for a little longer, until she heard the
sound of his car's engine starting up, and the sound of the car
disappearing down the road to the valley. Then she roused
herself. She decided to find a book, and walked back to the
hall, stepping over the cat and her kittens who were still
sunning themselves on the doorstep.

In the cool hallway she hesitated, uncertain which way to
go, then remembered the directions he had given her earlier.
She opened the door to her left, and found herself in what
must be his study. Bookcases covered the walls from floor to
ceiling; there were two desks, piles of papers, sofas piled with
cushions, a wide fireplace with ashes from a log fire. She
looked around her curiously, and opened the far door which
led into a large drawing room, with a grand piano, and tall
windows on to the terrace. But she felt a little uneasy, an
interloper, that she should not really be here, so she shut the
door, went to the bookshelves, and hurriedly selected a book
at random.

She still felt sleepy from the wine and the sun and the
journey, so she decided to go upstairs and read for a while in
the cool of her bedroom. Upstairs she found her cases and
unpacked, then, relieved to be alone, still feeling disturbed and
on edge as a result of their conversation, she lay down on the
wide white bed and opened the book.

A press cutting fell out from between the pages, and she
picked it up. It was a photograph of Laurence Martineau's
wedding. It was faded and yellowed, torn at the edges as if it
had been roughly pulled out from a newspaper in haste. 'At
Brompton Oratory yesterday, Laurence Martineau, 28, the
actor, was married to Miss Camilla Drew, with whom he is
appearing in *Hamlet* at . . .' The rest of the words had been

torn off at the corner. In the photograph was a group of people, Laurence Martineau in a morning suit, Camilla Drew in a beautiful white lace dress, two pages and two small bridesmaids in front of her.

Suddenly something he had said to her in London returned to her: 'I thought I knew my own mind when I was twenty-eight ...' Was that what he had meant? She felt miserable, a little guilty, as if she should not have found this, and she folded the piece of paper over and stuck it in the back of the book For some reason she could not explain, she did not want to be reminded of his marriage, of Camilla. She closed her eyes and lay back on the pillows and almost immediately fell asleep.

She slept badly, pursued with dreams. Camilla came to her in them, but she was not like the Camilla she had read about. She wasn't a sophisticated, beautiful woman, but a thin, pale wraith, malevolent, slightly mad, with her long pale hair streaming in the wind. Katy was trying to find someone, but wherever she turned she found Camilla ... They were in a street, then by the sea. She was standing on the edge of a tall cliff, and the gulls wheeled above her.

'Can't you see him?' a voice said. 'Look down there ...' then she felt the pressure of two small, cold hands on her back, and she was falling, falling ...

As she fell, she looked up, and Camilla stood at the top of the cliff, wrapped in Laurence Martineau's arms, and laughing that same thin, mad laugh. Gulls, cliffs, rocks, water, grass, sand. The world wheeled and tilted, and Katy knew with absolute certainty that she would drown.

Then she woke, and for a moment couldn't remember where she was. The edge of the dream was still with her, and the room seemed strange and unfamiliar. Then she felt the cool cotton of the bedcover, looked down and saw the book which had fallen to the floor, and remembered where she was. The afternoon came back to her, and it suddenly struck her that the newspaper picture on the floor was the only one of Camilla that she had seen in the house. The divorce had been acrimonious, she thought, so perhaps it was not surprising. Yet the place had no sense of her presence. Very much it was Laurence's house. It was as if Camilla had never been there She had been exiled, rubbed out. Perhaps that was why she came back so forcefully in dreams, Katy thought, and shivered. The room was cold.

She got up hastily, splashed her face with water, opened the shutters, and looked out. Warmth floated up from the flag-stones of the terrace, and the scent of flowers came into the room. Gradually the force of the dream slipped away, reality took hold again, and she felt better. Still, she felt as if she had—curiously—been warned. It would not do, she felt, to let herself become too involved, too influenced by what she had read, by the swift events of the past days which had so altered her life. Above all, she had better resolve there and then to treat this visit and this job as what it was—a temporary affair, a business arrangement, and one prompted by charity to boot.

No more thinking about Laurence Martineau, she told her-self sternly; pull yourself together and get on with the job. She promised herself to stay off awkward territory: no questions about the past, about why he no longer acted in the theatre; no comments about marriage and no callow remarks about plays he knew backwards and she had read only at school! She brushed her hair, put on the little jacket to her dress, smoothed the creases from her skirt, and resolved to stick to two glasses of wine at most and to give the best performance she could manage of the super-efficient personal secretary. As it happened, it proved quite easy.

When she went downstairs, she found him seated on the terrace, one of the cats on his lap. Katy made no sound as she stepped out of the doorway, because she was still wearing san-dals, and she had the impression he had not heard her. He was sitting near one of the cypress trees, looking out over the valley. He stroked the cat rhythmically, and absently, and on his face was that same haunted look she had seen before. He looked as if his eyes were scanning not the landscape but the territory of the past, and when he realised she was there, his manner was formal, polite, utterly distanced. They talked halt-ingly, but his mind seemed to be elsewhere.

Later Marie-Christine served them a wonderful dinner, and they sat inside, by the light of candles, with the great shutters opened to the cool of the night air. There was roasted guinea-fowl, another huge salad, pears baked in sugar and brandy. With it they drank a curious Provençal wine, a pale mauve pink, served chilled in deep glasses, and with the wine Laurence seemed to relax a little, though a certain tension never left him.

Katy asked questions about her job, about the region, about Marie-Christine and her family, and the time passed well enough. She congratulated herself that she had managed to avoid the subjects that had caused such sharp reactions in the past, and the sense of dislocation and unease she had felt when she awoke from her dream earlier that evening almost passed completely.

They had coffee by the fire in the drawing room, and the conversation became more desultory. Laurence stared into the flames, and seemed again abstracted. Katy was just going to excuse herself and retire to her room, when he got up suddenly and walked over to the window.

'You didn't tell me,' he said, looking out. 'You didn't say if there was any opposition to your coming here.'

'Opposition?'

'Well, it was all rather sudden. I would have thought that somebody—your family ...' He left the sentence un-completed.

'Well, there was a little,' she admitted, remembering the scene in her flat, and the comments of Bob, not to mention Jane's untactful remarks. 'My mother wasn't too keen on the idea, and some of my friends thought that ...' her voice trailed away.

'Thought what?' He turned sharply to face her.

'Oh, just thought that I should stay in London, look for another job in television, that's all,' she said hastily.

'I see. Your friends.'

There was a silence.

'But you didn't agree with them?'

'No,' she said, 'I wanted to come. I thought it would be so exciting to see Provence, and besides ...' she rushed on, aware that she was on somewhat difficult territory, 'besides, it was only for a few weeks, or a few months ...' She left the sentence hanging in the air, suddenly aware that what she had said was not exactly tactful or polite, implying she had come for a kind of glorified holiday. He gave her a long, cold look.

'Well,' he said briskly, 'we must make sure you see something of the region while you're here, so you won't have had a wasted journey. And, as you say, it's only for a brief time.

You'll be able to pick up the threads of your life in England very shortly. Your career or . . . the other alternatives.'

He turned back towards the window and closed the shutters, and Katy shivered involuntarily, whether at the cold breeze from the terrace or the cold tones of his voice, she couldn't be certain.

'Now,' he said, 'if you'll forgive me, I'm very tired, and we have some work to do in the morning. Could you come down to my study at nine-thirty, do you think? I always take breakfast very early, and Marie-Christine will bring yours to your room.'

Katy rose hastily to her feet and wished him goodnight. He answered abstractedly, hardly even looking in her direction.

She went up to her room feeling snubbed, irritated with herself, and once more on edge. It was some time before she felt able to sleep, and when she went to close her shutters and looked down on the terrace below it was very late. The sky was clear, the stars dazzlingly spread out across the great arc of the sky, and the moon was rising. But although it was so late, the terrace was not empty. Laurence Martineau was standing where she had seen him earlier. As she leant out and saw him, she thought for a moment that he turned swiftly away, as if he had been looking up at the house. But she couldn't be sure; he had his back to her and was standing, alone and motionless, with that curious stillness he possessed, looking out across the moonlit valley.

CHAPTER SIX

KATY slept badly and woke early next morning, as brilliant sunlight striped through the shutters into her room. She bathed, dressed, ate the delicious breakfast of fruit, and the coffee and croissants that Marie-Christine brought her. She was ready an hour before she was needed, and sat nervously in her room, wanting to go outside and yet curiously reluctant to begin the day. At nine-twenty she finally went downstairs, and into the study; Laurence Martineau was already seated at his desk, a pile of papers in front of him.

He looked up and gave her a brief nod.

'Good morning. You slept well?'

'Thank you, yes, very well.'

'Then we'll get down to work if we may.' He smiled formally. 'It's Sunday, of course, but there's a bit of a backlog—I hope you don't mind?'

'Not at all.'

'Generally speaking, I think it would be best if we worked in the mornings. In the afternoon it's still very hot—you may find you need a siesta . . . If we can catch up on things then we may have time to make a few expeditions. Now——'

He indicated the other desk, at right angles to his own. It was neatly arranged, and on it was a pile of letters and packets.

'Most of it you'll find pretty straightforward, I think. Letters from my agent and my accountant come to me. Everything else you can deal with.'

'Everything else?' Katy looked at the pile in some dismay.

'Certainly. Most of it will be fan letters; I don't want to read them, simply acknowledge them as pleasantly as you can. If they want photographs you'll find them in the files. There'll be requests for interviews too—refuse them all. It doesn't matter whether it's *The Times* or an American Ph.D. student wanting me to write his thesis for him. The answer is no; is that clear?'

Katy nodded.

'There will also be scripts. I don't want to read them. You can look over them if you have the time. If it's a film, and it sounds interesting, send it to my agent—it should have gone there in the first place. If it's a play, send it back and say I'm already committed. Any questions?'

Katy shook her head. It didn't sound much fun, she thought, and she was surprised he didn't even read scripts, but after yesterday she was in no mood to argue.

'Oh—and the telephone. I take no calls. There'll be very few in any case. Only my agent has the number; personal calls will come to me on my direct line. Should anyone else ring, get rid of them. I'm sure you can do it charmingly—you must have had plenty of practice when working for Hunt. Is that clear?'

'Perfectly clear,' she said dully.

'My secretary has left instructions for you, I think?' He indicated a neatly typed sheet of paper that lay in the otherwise empty OUT tray. 'That explains all the procedures, the filing system and so on. You'll find form letters to cover practically every contingency. If you're in doubt about anything, just ask.'

'Oh, I will,' she said.

'And don't let yourself get too involved in it, will you?' He gave her a frosty smile. 'You'll find some of the fan letters can be—well, a little extreme. Most are just requests for pictures or autographs. But some of the women can get a little persistent. Take no notice. They get a maximum of three replies; after that, tear the letters up. Is that understood? If someone writes more than three times, they're either infatuated, or hysterical. Either way, I'm not interested. Suicide threats are par for the course. You'll take them in your stride, I presume?'

'I'll try,' said Katy, compressing her lips, and wondering how he could be so callous—still, wasn't that exactly how everyone had always described him? She was seeing another side to him now, she thought, and she'd do well to remember it was there.

'It won't bother you my being here?' He indicated his own desk. 'I generally work here in the mornings. I'll try not to disturb you.'

'Not at all.'

She sat down and drew the secretary's instructions towards

her. It looked every bit as efficient as she had expected. Laurence lingered by her desk for a moment, and then abruptly turned away. Within minutes, absorbed in work, he gave every appearance of having forgotten her presence. Katy read through the numbered list, acutely conscious that he was sitting just three feet away from her. But her spirits lifted a little as she read; yes, really, it did seem quite straight-forward . . .

Quietly she began to work. She checked through the filing system, making sure she understood how it worked. She found the supplies of plain stationery, headed simply with his name. She opened the pile of letters and packets and began to go through them. After a while, she became quite absorbed in her task. The sun slanted into the room through the open windows; once she thought she heard the sound of Marie-Christine's children playing in the courtyard below, and the clattering sound of pots and pans came from across the hall in the kitchen. Otherwise the silence was total. When she had sorted through the pile of mail, which was much as he had predicted, she found the form letters, and uncovered the type-writer. It was a new electric Olivetti, a far cry from the kind of battered machine which researchers at Metropolitan had had to make do with, but she typed well, and she soon grew accus-tomed to it. She wondered, as she began typing, if the noise would disturb him, but he seemed totally unaffected by it. His eyes never lifted from the pages in front of him; she might have been totally invisible, inaudible. She was quite glad that in order to type she had to turn with her back to him, for she found such absorption a little unnerving.

She wasn't sure how long she worked—a couple of hours perhaps. Suddenly the telephone rang—not the one on her desk, but the one on his—the direct line.

The sudden shrill of the bell made her jump, and she spun round. He was watching her, she saw, her eyes widening, with that thoughtful shadowed expression on his face that she was coming to know so well. At the sound of the bell it was replaced with a grimace of annoyance. He picked up the re-ceiver, and quickly she turned back to the typewriter.

'Yes,' she heard.

Then there was a long silence. She clattered the keys, feeling embarrassed and in the way.

'Very well,' she heard. 'No, that's impossible. What?'

She stole a look at him as she unrolled the letter from the typewriter, and turned to reach for an envelope. His face was unreadable, without animation.

'This afternoon, then. No, not before then. Certainly.'

He hung up. He looked agitated, she saw, all the customary composure momentarily gone. He picked up a thin silver paper-knife which lay on his desk, and tapped his papers with it. Then with an abrupt gesture he pushed them aside. They knocked against a tall pile of letters and memoranda, and they all cascaded to the floor. Before she could stop herself, Katy jumped up and began to gather them together.

'Leave them,' he said.

She paused, looking up enquiringly.

'Leave them, I said!' his voice was harsh.

Silently she got up and went back to her desk.

'I'll do it later,' he said, more gently, as if aware he had sounded rude and abrupt. 'I had planned to take you down to the sea this afternoon,' he went on. 'Now I'm afraid that won't be possible. I shall have to go out. Will you be able to manage here, do you think?'

She nodded, feeling a curious lurch of disappointment.

'Please,' she said, 'don't worry about me. There's plenty to do here. I'll just get on with some work.'

Laurence gave her a tight smile.

'Such industry,' he said, with a note of sarcasm in his voice. 'I'm very impressed.'

'I'm sure you're not,' she said quickly, 'but all the same . . .'

'All the same we'll do something else this evening,' he said, with an odd note of defiance in his voice. 'I'll take you down to the village. I know . . .' He hesitated. 'I'll take you to Mass in the village church. You're not Catholic, of course?'

She shook her head, taken aback as usual by the swiftness with which his moods changed, the suddenness with which he made plans.

'I was.' He shrugged. 'No longer. But the church is very beautiful, and the service is still held in Latin—you might like it. If you behave, you can shake hands afterwards with the *curé* and I'll take you for dinner at the café in the square. It's not Angelo's, but . . .'

'I should like that very much,' she said quickly.

'Should you?' He smiled. 'Then we shall both have something to look forward to. Now—if there are no problems . . .'

'None.'

'Then I'll leave you to your work.' He looked at his watch. 'I'll tell Marie-Christine to give you lunch on the terrace at one. Please don't work after that. It's not necessary, you know. I'm not a slavedriver.' Abruptly he pushed the papers on his desk into a pile and turned to the door. 'Now, if you'll excuse me?' he said, and without waiting for any answer, he was gone.

Katy had plenty of time to speculate as to who had telephoned, and why—having said he would meet whoever it was that afternoon—he then left before noon. The rest of the day passed very slowly, and it was past five before, as she sat outside on the terrace looking across the valley, she heard his car come up the steep road and park in the courtyard below. Wherever he had been, it had put him in a far better humour, she noted, for he came bounding up the steps, all trace of that morning's hauteur and formality quite gone. With rapid strides he crossed the terrace, until he reached her side. Quickly she rose to her feet.

'You don't have to get up,' he said, smiling. 'You gave a very good impression of the perfect employee this morning, but you don't have to take it to extremes.' He paused, and she saw him look with what seemed approval at what she was wearing.

'Very tactful,' he said, indicating the simple dark dress she had put on, with long sleeves and a high neckline. 'All the village women cloak themselves in black from head to foot, and it might upset them to see an outsider in church who didn't observe the formalities. Such things matter here, very much. Are you ready to leave now?'

Katy nodded.

'Oh, here.' He handed her a small parcel, wrapped with silk ribbon. 'For you.'

She stared, then took the parcel from him.

'Open it,' he said impatiently.

With trembling fingers, and a sudden feeling of excitement, she untied the ribbon and folded back the delicate tissue paper.

'Oh!' She caught her breath. Inside the parcel was the most exquisite scarf, of the finest black lace, hand-stitched, like a Spanish mantilla. As she opened it out, it spun from her fingers like the finest, most delicate cobweb. She felt her colour rise in her cheeks with pleasure and surprise and she knew Laurence was watching her.

'For Mass the head should be covered,' he said. 'I thought you might not have anything suitable with you. Of course, if you don't like it . . .'

'Like it? Why, it's exquisite, it's the loveliest . . .'

'Then put it on. We should go.'

Carefully she shook out the folds, and wrapped it over her head and around her throat.

'Is that right?' She tilted her face up to him for approval.

He was looking at her intently, his dark eyes unreadable; they were standing very close.

'Perhaps . . . like this.'

He reached across and made a small adjustment, so that more of her hair was covered. As he did so, his fingers brushed her cheek, and she felt a sudden electric pulse shoot through her whole body.

'Yes, like that,' he said. The hand which, for a second, lingered against her skin was quickly withdrawn. She thought she saw admiration in his eyes, but he merely nodded formally. 'Just so. The idea is not to enhance a woman's beauty, but to make her look . . .' he hesitated.

'Quiet as a nun?' she quoted, her eyes dancing, for she fancied him for some reason discomfited.

'Something like that,' he said drily. 'Shall we go?'

The church was tiny, perhaps fourteenth-century, with low rounded arches, and flickering shadows. It was lit by hundreds of candles, placed by the Stations of the Cross, in front of the statues of the Virgin, by the altar. The air was thick with incense, and the scent of lilies. They took their places at the back of the church, and Katy noted that although he made the customary brief bow of obeisance towards the altar before he took his place, he did not—as the villagers all did—cross himself with the holy water as they came in the narrow arched door. The service began, and as the complicated rituals of the Mass succeeded each other, Katy soon forgot her own un-familiarity with the procedures. She stood and sat, knelt and stood, following those who were in the body of the church in front of her. Laurence Martineau, beside her on the cold oak pew, murmured the words of the Latin service with the familiarity of the childhood Catholic.

She tried to wrench her mind away from him, for she was deeply conscious of his presence so close to her, and to concentrate on the service. Once, kneeling to pray, she glanced towards him quickly, and saw that although he knelt, he did not close his eyes. Instead they stayed, unwaveringly, on the tiny altar, and the gold and white figure of the priest before them. The bell rang for the elevation of the Host; the tiny church was filled with a deep, almost slumbrous silence. Then, as villagers began to file out from the pews and go up to take Communion, he touched her arm lightly.

'We'll leave now, if you don't mind,' he said in a low voice.

Quietly he stood, and she followed him out into the cool night air.

'You don't take Communion?' she asked, and instantly cursed herself for her stupidity.

'Not since my divorce,' he said shortly.

The church was at the top of a steep hill on the edge of the village. Down below them, in the square, Katy could see lights, and hear an accordion playing, very softly. Apart from that the night was heavy with silence, the air balmy and cool against her skin. The road was cobbled and dimly lit. As they walked down, she stumbled in her thin London shoes, and Laurence put out a hand to steady her. He kept the hand there, she noticed, holding her lightly above the elbow, until they reached the paving in the square. Then he removed it.

With a grave formality, rather as if he were an uncle with a visiting niece, he ushered her into the tiny café that opened on to the square. He nodded and exchanged a few words with the men who stood at the bar, with a couple who were playing pool, then he led them into a small room at the back, with a few tables and wooden chairs, and they sat down in the corner. A young girl of perhaps fourteen came to take their order, and brought them bread and a carafe of wine. They were the only people eating, although delicious cooking smells were wafting through from the kitchen. Bursts of laughter came from the men outside in the bar. Katy looked around her with pleasure.

'What a lovely place,' she said.

Laurence Martineau smiled. 'I like it,' he said. 'It will fill up later, after Mass. It's run by a cousin of Marie-Christine's, who's a marvellous cook. Wait and see.'

He looked more relaxed than she had ever seen him, she thought, and she noted that he was treated here without ceremony.

'Do you often come here?' she asked curiously, for she wondered very much how he usually spent his time here in Provence, so cut off, at his choice, from the outside world.

'Often enough,' he said. 'It gives Marie-Christine a night off. And I like it.'

'You must miss all this when you're away,' she said. 'It's such a beautiful place. And so peaceful. I feel as if I'd been here for weeks. I can hardly believe I was in London yesterday.'

'It has that effect,' he said drily. 'But I expect you'll forget it just as quickly when you go back. For you it's just an interlude—a summer interlude. It's different for me. I was brought up here.'

For a moment she nearly challenged him on that statement, but she thought better of it. The reminder of her return somehow chilled her feelings. And she was wary in conversation with him now, for she knew how suddenly it could take a wrong turning.

'Did you come often to Provence as a child?' she said instead, determined this time her questions should be innocuous.

'Very often,' he said. 'I was passed around from pillar to post—school in England, holidays in Paris with my mother ... but I was most often here. I made my first communion here, with the priest you saw tonight. You'll meet him later. He'll come in and drink one *marc* and make it last the best part of an hour, and if he sees me he'll give me a lecture— maybe even a peñance.'

She smiled. 'Maybe you need it,' she said.

'Oh, I do,' he said lazily. 'Father Bernard lives in hope I'll repent of my evil ways. And tonight he'll have hopes for me— I'm certain of it.'

'Why tonight?'

'Because of you, of course.' He looked at her mockingly.

'He'll have seen me at the Mass, because he has eyes like a hawk, and that will be a point in my favour. And then I'm with a pure young woman, with her head reverently covered, who looks a little like a novice just at this moment. And he's sure to think she's having a good influence on me.' He smiled
'And he would be quite right. You are.'

Katy laughed. 'Well, I'm flattered to hear it,' she said. 'Though I doubt it very much if it's true. What hellish deeds am I keeping you from?'

He looked at her solemnly. 'Very hellish deeds,' he said. 'If you weren't here I should probably be totally debauched. I'd have drunk a bottle of brandy by now, at least, and seduced all the village women.'

'And do you do that every night when I'm not here?'

'But of course.' He smiled. 'Especially on Sundays.'

'When do you rest?'

He laughed. 'Never,' he said firmly. 'Ask the *curé*.'

'Then I'm glad I'm here,' she said lightly.

He raised his glass in an ironic salute. 'And I'm glad too,' he said. '*Santé.*'

Soon afterwards the small café began to fill up; the food arrived, and it was as delicious, Katy found, as he had promised. In the bar the accordion player played more loudly, and a woman began to sing, in a high, sweet clear voice. Katy listened to her entranced, trying to make out the words of the song. After a while she sighed.

'It's no good,' she said. 'My French is so rusty. I can't understand, and it sounds so lovely. What is she singing?'

'A love song.'

'A happy one? It sounds happy.'

'I'm afraid not.' He looked away.

'An unhappy one, then?'

'But of course. It's a Provençal song. They're very truthful.'

The shadow had come over his face again, and it was no surprise to her when he gestured to the waitress and quickly paid the bill.

'We'll go home now, I think,' he said.

Katy put down her tiny cup of black coffee untasted, for he had risen abruptly. Courteously, formally, he escorted her out towards the bar. Seated by the door, just as Laurence

Martineau had foretold, was the priest. He was playing dominoes, and at his elbow was a tiny glass of *marc*. When he saw them he rose, an old bent figure, with a face so tanned and lined by the sun that he looked like a man who spent all day in the fields. Warmly he grasped Laurence Martineau's arm, and launched into a flood of heavily accented French. *La jeune fille anglaise* was all Katy caught; formally she was introduced to him, and to her surprise he grasped her hand with enormous strength, then held her at arm's length. His eyes, a sharp, brilliant blue, searched her face quickly, then he turned back to the actor with a broad and most unpriestly smile, and another torrent of words. Laurence Martineau also smiled, and gently disengaged them. Moments later they were out in the dark street, heavy now with the rasping sound of cicadas, and lit by the darting light of fireflies.

They drove back to La Bayardière in silence through the still fields. As Katy looked at the profile of the man beside her, the eyes shadowed, the expression closed, she was reminded of a poem she had had to learn at school. How had it begun? *Je suis le veuf, le ténébreux, l'inconsolé* . . . I am the widower, the dark one, the inconsolable. It suited him, she thought, except of course that Laurence Martineau was no widower, but a divorced man . . .

In the hall way she hesitated, half reluctant to go to bed, half hoping that he might suggest coffee, that the conversation which had gone so well earlier in the evening might continue. But he turned from barring the door as if surprised she was still there.

'Goodnight, Katharine,' he said abruptly.

'Goodnight,' she said. 'And . . . thank you for my present, and for taking me to the church . . .'

'Not at all. I'll see you in the morning.'

He went into his study and closed the door. Soon afterwards, upstairs, she heard the sounds of music. He was playing a record—Mozart, she thought—a little too loud. It was still playing at two o'clock when finally, exhausted, she fell asleep.

After that first day, Katy settled into a loose routine. Each morning she worked as she had that first day, and usually Laurence Martineau did also. There was no repetition of the call on his direct line which had come that first morning—

indeed, the telephones rarely rang at all. But he was, quite often, absent. Sometimes he would announce the previous day that the next he would have to go out; sometimes he left without warning, even cancelling plans they had talked of the night before over dinner. Once, when Katy had gone up to her room to fetch something in the middle of the morning, she heard him talking on the telephone upstairs as she returned to the study. His voice was muffled; she heard the click as the receiver was replaced. That morning he looked agitated—just as he had the first day, she thought. And once again, without explanation, he left her alone in the afternoon, returning late, his face grey with strain and tiredness, when she was half way through dinner.

To begin with, these sudden departures had made her intensely curious; on one of her visits to the village she had even bought a gossipy newspaper that chronicled the comings and goings of film stars and jet-setters to Cannes and Nice, and had scanned it, wondering if one of the women whose name had been connected with his was staying nearby. Then she despised herself for her action, and angrily threw the paper away; after all, it was none of her business, she had no right to care.

After that, she tried to put the whole matter out of her head, and though she was sometimes racked with a desire to ask him where he had been, what he had been doing, she never did. Once, in a roundabout way, she had asked him if he had had a good afternoon. She had received a cold stare and a dismissive remark that told her nothing. She didn't repeat the experiment.

When she was left alone, if she had finished the work for that day, she would go for long walks in the beautiful countryside around. Sometimes she helped Marie-Christine in the kitchen, and in reward was shown how to cook some of the deceptively simple dishes which they enjoyed day by day. Her French improved, a little. Sometimes she would try to write letters—to her mother, to Jane. But, though she sent them, she wasn't pleased with them. She found it oddly difficult to describe what she had been doing, where she had been. She wrote a lot about the countryside, about Marie-Christine and her children. She hardly mentioned Laurence Martineau; it seemed easier not.

He, good as his word, took her out several times on the days when he did not make one of his abrupt disappearances. One afternoon they went riding in the hills behind the house; another time to some deserted beaches nearby. On market day, he took her into Toulon, with a shopping list provided by Marie-Christine, and firm instructions that she should practice her French.

The market at Toulon was huge, spread out in the great, white dusty square at the heart of the old town. Katy caught her breath when she first saw it, it was so sumptuous, so extravagantly beautiful. Under the shade of the pollarded trees with their white-painted trunks, it was as if all the bounties of the earth had been laid out. The air was heavy with the scent of fruit and flowers and herbs. Piled high on the stalls were great mounds of shiny purple aubergines, sun-ripened Mediterranean tomatoes, tiny crisp green courgettes, baskets filled with fresh basil and oregano and thyme bound into bunches. There were three kinds of garlic, red shallots, onions in strings. Trestles were piled high with peaches, nectarines, heavy purple figs, their skins just bursting with ripeness. There were gipsy women there, from the Camargue, selling ribbons and trinkets, fishermen unloading that morning's catch. The sun shone brilliantly, and in the corner of the square an accordionist was playing.

Katy's heart lifted with pleasure. Laurence Martineau held back, an ironic smile on his lips, as he watched her dart from stall to stall, loading the deep straw baskets Marie-Christine had given her. She was very brown now from the sun, and her tanned skin glowed against the thin white cotton of her dress. To her surprise, the stallholders showed no impatience with her halting French. They teased her, laughed, and her confidence grew as she found she could understand them, even though their French, like Marie-Christine's, was the rough patois of the south.

'*Mademoiselle! Jolie mademoiselle!*'

One of the stallholders, a young man, very small and dark, with a brilliant red scarf around his tanned neck, was calling to her. Katy spun round.

'*Vous voulez des pêches, mademoiselle?*' He gestured to the peaches piled high before him. '*Elles sont bonnes!*' He smiled, as she reached out to touch them. '*Les plus belles du marché, comme vous, mademoiselle!'*

Laurence Martineau had moved to her side, and she saw him raise an ironic eyebrow.

'Well, beautiful Katy,' he said with a smile. 'Can you resist a compliment like that?'

'Certainly I can!' She laughed at him.

The stallholder glanced from her to the tall, dark man at her side, and raising his eyes heavenward, in a dramatic gesture of adoration, he laid one hand across his heart.

'Mille excuses, monsieur,' he said, his eyes gleaming wickedly. *'Jolie madame . . . Je plaisante, c'est tout . . .'*

Keeping her face composed, Katy took her time, though eventually she bought some kilos of his peaches. She turned away finally, pretending not to notice the extravagantly gallant kiss which was blown in her direction, and returned to Laurence Martineau's side. He was watching her still, a smile on his lips.

'You're learning,' he said, taking the laden baskets from her.

'I know I am,' Katy said proudly. 'In London I'd never dare poke the fruit about like that. But Marie-Christine says you must. She says if you don't they don't respect you—they sell you rubbish. And he did have the best peaches, too,' she added quickly, as she saw that mocking glint come into Laurence Martineau's eyes.

She held out one of the peaches to him, amber and pink, with a heady scent of the sun. He took it, and looked at her appraisingly.

'Tu deviendras une vraie ménagère, Kate,' he said smilingly.

She felt herself blushing at his unexpected use of the familiar '*tu*' rather than the more formal '*vous*'.

'*Ménagère*—that's housewife, isn't it?'

'Oh, better than that, Kate,' he said. 'The French—for once—put it better than we do. The *ménagère* is all things—mother, wife, provider. For a Frenchman it's the ultimate in praise.'

She laughed and pushed her hair back from her face.

'I'd have thought a Frenchman's ultimate term of praise for a woman was "*maîtresse*",' she said teasingly.

She saw his eyebrows lift just a fraction.

'Mistress? Yes, well, you're right in a sense. But although Frenchmen boast about their mistresses a good deal, it's an unbreakable law that they always return to their wives. Now . . .' he put the peach back in the basket, and lightly took her arm, 'I think we should leave. The stallholder you bargained with so fearlessly has been struck dumb with admiration, and I don't think it's entirely your bargaining skills he admires. I think I'll take you home, before you disgrace me by getting propositioned in the middle of Toulon market. Shall we go?'

But Katy found it difficult to tear herself away from the noise and the beauty of it all. She bought some trinkets she thought might amuse her sisters, and a postcard for Lindy, and in the end, instead of returning straight to La Bayardière they stopped at a pavement café, where Laurence Martineau ordered some *pastis*.

Following his example, she poured water on to the clear liquid, so it turned a creamy colour in the long iced glasses. The scent of anise rose up strongly, and she wrinkled her nose.

Laurence smiled. 'Try it,' he said. 'It's what everyone here drinks, and it's very refreshing. But sip it slowly, it's very strong.'

She followed his advice, the odd taste growing on her. The cool liquid exploded with warmth in her stomach, the sun shone down on their table strongly. Luxuriating in the dual warmth, Katy stretched languorously. She felt so happy, she thought, so relaxed. She'd like to stay here just this way, for ever and ever . . .

Laurence Martineau looked relaxed too, she thought, looking at him covertly as he leaned back in his chair, his eyes moving lazily over the market crowds. How endless time could feel here, she thought, how unpressurised. How different from London. She glanced down to the table and the garish colours of the postcard momentarily brought that world back to her. How long ago it felt—her job, the day Lindy had rung up, the day she had first met this strange man who now sat so composedly beside her . . .

'You never told me,' she began suddenly, feeling emboldened by the peace of the place, his teasing, his attitude of relaxation. He turned his head enquiringly, and she broke off, fingering the corner of Lindy's postcard.

'Yes?' The dark eyes met hers.

'You never told me how you came to do the interview with Dick Hunt,' she went on, voicing at last the question she had burned to ask for days.

'No,' he said lightly, 'I didn't.'

'I just wondered . . .' she hesitated, but there had been no rebuff in his voice, 'how you came to know him. Whether you and he had ever met before.'

There was a pause. The dark gaze wavered just for a second.

'We had met before,' he said finally, flatly. She saw him look away, and thought he meant to add no more, but then he turned back to her swiftly, with an odd intensity, as if he had suddenly decided something. 'We first met ten years ago,' he said, and she saw his hand tighten momentarily on the stem of his glass. 'At one time I knew him very well. But we hadn't met for some years.'

Katy sipped her *pastis*, and the silence lengthened. How odd, she thought, her mind suddenly racing. They had both pretended not to know each other, and yet she had been right, she had felt certain . . .

'How did you meet?' she asked curiously. 'Did Dick ever try to interview you before . . .?'

Laurence Martineau made a quick gesture to the waiter, who disappeared inside the café for the bill.

'No,' he said slowly. 'No, nothing like that.' He hesitated, and she could see he was forcing himself to speak. 'We were introduced at the first-night party for my Hamlet, I think.' He sounded vague, but somehow Katy had the impression he remembered the incident only too clearly, in spite of his tone. He turned away to pay the bill, and then turned back. Their eyes locked for a second.

'My ex-wife introduced us,' he said. 'As I recall.'

A thousand questions immediately rose up in Katy's mind. It was the first time since she had come to France that he had ever referred directly to Camilla. She had a curious sensation for a moment that time had stopped. The noise of the market was blotted out as his eyes searched her face. But something stopped her from asking anything further, and his hand briefly, almost accidentally, covered her own. As quickly he removed it, and rose to his feet.

'*Jolie madame.*' He made a gesture towards his heart in good imitation of the red-scarfed stallholder, and his lips smiled, although his eyes looked dulled and pained. 'Shall we go home now? I think it's time we impressed Marie-Christine with the fruits of your Provençal shopping skills.' Without pausing, he led the way back through the market to his Lagonda, and Katy followed him silently. So Dick Hunt *had* known Camilla. Had he been a close friend? *Had* it been him with Camilla in that newspaper photograph? But she shrugged the speculations away. Probably not, she thought, feeling suddenly tired. And anyway, what difference did it make to her?

The next Sunday—when she had been there a week, Katy thought happily, though it felt like a month—she had hoped he might take her again to Mass in the village. But that day, she sensed immediately, he was in his worst mood, cold, unreachable and sarcastic. The barriers that seemed momentarily to have been dropped had gone up again, even more fiercely. He left the house in mid-morning, saying only that he would return late, and not to keep dinner for him. Disappointed, she went instead with Marie-Christine and Gaston and the children to Mass, and when they returned, seeing the big house empty and dark, she gladly accepted their invitation to eat with them down in their courtyard, sitting out under the stars and looking up at the sky through the vine-leaves of the pergola. Marie-Christine was worried. The next day she had to visit '*la vieille grand'mère de la famille*', she explained. The old lady was ill, and Gaston had to work, and she didn't know what she would do with the children . . .

Katy leaned impulsively across the long table. 'But there's no problem,' she said, attempting her best French. 'If you go in the afternoon, I can take the children. We can walk down to the beach and play there, I've plenty of time, you've no need to worry . . .'

And so it was arranged. Katy had no opportunity to tell Laurence Martineau that night, for she did not see him, although she heard him return in the early hours of the morning. That night she had the dream again, the one she had had the first afternoon, about Camilla, and she woke feeling exhausted and unaccountably nervous, that thin malevolent laughter still ringing in her ears. Laurence Martineau, she noted, also looked drawn and tired, and when she asked his permission to take the children out that afternoon, he gave it absently. They worked side by side in silence, but, by the end of the morning, his spirits seemed to have revived.

'If you like,' he said casually, as she began to tidy her desk, 'I'll take you and the children in the car. We can take a picnic. There's a better beach we can go to that's a little farther away. Unless you'd rather be on your own, of course?'

She knew her face lit up immediately at the suggestion, and that he noted her reaction.

'Oh no, please do come,' she said quickly, trying to sound casual. 'It would be much more fun.'

Just before one they set off in the Lagonda. Katy had written some letters the previous day, and she put them on the front seat while she helped the three children pile excitedly into the back of the car. As she turned to get in, Laurence Martineau leaned across, picked them up and handed them to her. She saw his eyes flick over the top envelope. It was a letter to Bob; Dr Robert Parrish, St James's Hospital, it read; her writing, rounded and upright, could be read clearly at arm's length. Laurence Martineau let in the gears abruptly and accelerated away. He stopped in the village, so she could post the letters, and when she got back into the car she could read the irritation of his features.

'You're quite well, I hope?' He glared at her.

'Yes,' she said, not immediately following his meaning. 'Why do you ask?'

'Writing to an English doctor?'

'Oh, not as a doctor,' she said quickly. 'As a friend. Bob Parrish is an old friend. You saw him once, that day . . .'

'Ah yes. The young man with the roses.' He blasted his horn at some chickens pecking in the roadway, and the children behind squealed delightedly.

'You're keeping in touch with your friends while you're here then?' he said unpleasantly.

'But of course.' His tone stung her. After all, she thought, why ever shouldn't she write to her friends? It was surely nothing to do with him. As it happened, it was the first time she had written to Bob, and it was a short, dull letter, she thought ruefully. Somehow there hadn't seemed much to say . . .

'No doubt you're impatient to be back in England with them all?' His tone was now so overtly rude that she glanced at him in surprise.

'No,' she said quietly. 'Not at all. I love being here. I don't want to . . .' She broke off. To go back, she had been about to say, she thought with surprise. Was that true? She pushed the thought away. It was so lovely here, so warm, so beautiful, anyone would feel that.

'Don't want to what?' He kept his face averted, his eyes on the narrow winding road.

'Oh, nothing. I'm not in a hurry to go back to England or to English weather, that's all,' she said lightly. 'My mother says it's been raining all week. Besides, I'm enjoying being a secretary.'

'Are you now?' He gave a grim smile. 'How lucky for everybody.'

Katy turned her face away, looked at the landscape, pointed things out to the children. There was no talking to him when he was in this mood, she thought crossly. Perhaps if she kept quiet, it would pass as suddenly as it came.

Indeed, during lunch, his mood did seem to lift. They had found a tiny deserted beach, and ate lunch in the shade of some olive trees that grew at the edge of the sand. Bruno, the eldest of Marie-Christine's children, was twelve, and spoke a little English, which he learned at the village school. He practised it proudly at the meal, asking for everything in English, and teaching the words patiently to his two little sisters. They were a little shyer, and a little scared of the tall dark man who carefully peeled their peaches for them, and ceremoniously cut up their cheese and pâté. They huddled next to Katy, still wary of him, their dark hair spilling out over her white cotton dress.

After lunch they all lay lazily in the warm dappled shade. Laurence showed Bruno how to whittle a piece of driftwood into a rough boat. Katy talked softly to the two girls, who— luckily, she thought—didn't mind her schoolgirl French. She told them about her home, and her sisters, and their dolls, and how in the summer, in Suffolk, they had once made a tree-house in the garden . . . It was incredibly peaceful, she thought, with just the sound of the waves lapping the beach, and the light breeze riffling the leaves of the olive tree. She was almost asleep; Bruno and Laurence Martineau were absorbed in their task, and she thought they paid her no attention. But after a little while Bruno looked up at her, slyly, his dark eyes dancing.

'*Vous avez combien de soeurs*, Mademoiselle Katy?' he asked.

'Three, Bruno,' she said lazily. 'Two older, and one younger—about your age.'

He asked their names, and she told him. He smiled.

'*Les plus âgées, elles sont mariées*, Mademoiselle Katy?'

'Yes, they are married, Bruno,' she said, watching the light filtering through the leaves. 'They have babies of their own . . .'

'*Mais vous, vous n'êtes pas mariée?*'

She sat up hurriedly, aware that Laurence was watching her intently.

'No, Bruno,' she said quickly. 'No, I'm not married.'

'*Pourquoi*, Mademoiselle Katy?'

How could she have forgotten how inquisitive small boys could be? she thought crossly, feeling embarrassed although, she told herself, there was no reason.

'Why not? Oh, because I haven't met the right man yet, I expect,' she said lightly.

'*Quel dommage,*' said the boy.

Laurence Martineau smiled and stretched. His eyes glittered dangerously. 'Yes, it is a shame, isn't it, Bruno?' he said mockingly, his eyes on Katy. 'But I've no doubt the situation will be remedied.'

'*Comment?*'

He had spoken in English and the boy had not understood. Katy rose to her feet hastily.

'Well, I'm going to swim,' she said. 'I'll race you to the sea, Bruno.'

She had put her bikini on under her dress, and she turned away modestly to take that off—it unbuttoned down the front—conscious that Laurence Martineau was lying back under the olives, still watching her with that infuriating mocking expression on his face.

She took her dress off quickly, keeping her back to the trees, and then without a backward glance fled down to the water, the children laughing happily in pursuit. They played there contentedly at the edge of the sea for some while, the two girls paddling and making castles and moats, Bruno showing off how well he could do the crawl. She and Bruno laughed and splashed, and Katy felt happy and relaxed. She almost forgot about the tall dark figure, almost out of sight now by the trees. Perhaps he had gone to sleep, she thought.

After a while, leaving Bruno in charge, and the children intent on catching a little sand crab, she left them at the water's edge, and swam lazily out to some rocks. The water was like warm silk against her skin, profound and yet clear. She lay and floated lazily for a while, revelling in the sun, then pulled herself on to the flat rocks, where she could lie, and still keep an eye on the children. She was deep in thought, paddling her palms in the water, watching the sea water gradually dry on her golden oiled skin, when she suddenly felt a shadow fall over her. Abruptly she turned, startled. Laurence Martineau was just pulling himself up on to the rocks beside her.

Curiously, her immediate instinct was to cover herself, and her hands flew to the thin top of her bikini and the curve of her breasts above it. He saw the movement and smiled sardonically.

'How modest,' he said. 'There's no need, you know. On most of these beaches no one bothers with swimming costumes.'

He sat down next to her on the rocks, the water rippling over his tanned, lean body. She felt his gaze rake over her, and to her confusion and anger she felt herself blushing. He looked at her in a way she had never seen a man look before, with a kind of naked hunger, and she felt as if his dark eyes were burning into her skin. Momentarily she remembered his jest that night in the village café. He might not have seduced all the village women, but he must certainly have seduced many others—probably without much difficulty, she thought, turning her eyes away from his hard man's body, the thick hair on his chest, the brief swimming trunks.

'Are the children all right?' she asked defensively, craning her head to see where they still played happily at the edge of the sea.

'They're fine,' he said quickly. 'Don't worry about them. They're quite safe, or I wouldn't have left them.' He smiled. 'You've charmed them thoroughly, you know,' he went on gently. 'Bruno especially. You've made another slave for life . . .'

'Another?' she said curiously.

'Oh, I'm sure there are plenty of others, aren't there, Kate?'

She felt rather than saw his eyes turn away from her, scanning the horizon.

'You're very good with children, you know,' he went on, more abruptly. 'Bruno's right. You should be married, with babies of your own.'

'Some day,' she muttered, resting her head on her arms and closing her eyes. A mental image of Bob came into her mind, the evening at home when he had first asked her to marry him. Her memory of him was curiously inexact, she realised, blurred, like an out-of-focus snapshot.

'Tell me, Kate, have you ever been in love? Have you ever had a lover?'

'*What?*' She whirled around to face him.

'Don't look so shocked.' He was looking at her intently. 'You're twenty-three, after all. You haven't spent your life in a convent.'

'Why should you ask?' she countered, totally thrown that he should suddenly be so outspoken, he, who always avoided all personal questions like the plague.

'For the most obvious of reasons. Because I want to know the answer.'

'I don't think you have any right to ask. And it's certainly none of your concern,' she said hotly.

He looked at her for a long moment, then away, as if suddenly bored.

'I think I know the answers to both questions anyway,' he said finally. 'They're written all over your face . . . and your body.'

'Little Miss Iceberg, you mean?' she cried, feeling suddenly furiously upset.

He shook his head; his hand briefly brushed hers.

'Not at all,' he said quickly, and she saw her words had stung him. 'I didn't mean . . .'

'It doesn't matter,' she rose impulsively to her feet. 'I'm going back to the beach . . .'

'As you wish.'

He moved more quickly than she, and was in the water before her. 'Let me help you,' he called. 'Be careful—the rocks at the edge are sharp!'

But she ignored his hand in her anger and haste, began to lower herself into the water, and lost her footing. As she fell, his arms caught her, wrapped strongly around her, and held her. Suddenly they were both in the sea, washed tightly against one another, so she felt every line of his hard body pressing against hers. Involuntarily she caught her breath in her throat in a soft moan. Her mouth was against the skin of his neck, her breasts pressed against his heart, their legs intertwined. The memory of the time he had kissed her, by the canal, a memory she had kept carefully at bay ever since, rushed back, and she felt pleasure flood through every vein in her body.

'Dear God, Kate . . .' His mouth was by her ear, her long hair washing against him. His voice sounded odd, and roughened, and her whole body trembled in his arms. Blindly, not daring to look at him, scarcely knowing what was happening, she let the waves lap her body against his, her lips parted, and his grip on her tightened with new urgency . . .

'Mademoiselle Katy!'

The shrill call brought her back to consciousness. Instantly she broke away from him; he let her go, then swam beside her as she made for the shore.

'You're all right?' he asked, as if nothing had happened. And indeed, she thought, what had happened? Nothing at all, except in her own mind. She had been saved from a nasty fall, that was all.

'I'm fine,' she said. 'Thank you.'

She saw him smile mockingly, then he veered away, increasing his pace, and reaching the beach with an easy, elegant crawl, minutes before she did. The children were fine, she saw with relief. The cry had signified no more than the finding of a particularly large crab.

They all had tea on the beach, no mention was made of what had happened. Laurence retreated once more behind a façade of teasing courtesy. Gradually Katy relaxed again. His questions had disturbed her—but after all, there was no real reason why they should have done. They had spent a lot of time together now. There was no reason, she thought, watching him as he played ball with the children, why he shouldn't want to know more about her private life. If it had been anyone else, she would have felt no embarrassment in answering . . .

They left the beach late, the children exhausted and sleepy, and deposited them happily with a grateful Marie-Christine.

Katy took more time than usual changing that evening, and put on the white dress she had worn the day Laurence Martineau came to her flat in London. As she had then, she tied her hair back with blue ribbon, and then, feeling nervous, went down to the kitchen. She had arranged that evening, as a surprise, she—and not Marie-Christine—would cook dinner for them. Laurence was nowhere to be seen, although she could hear music coming from his study. She was quite glad of his absence, she thought, for she knew she would cook better without that dark speculative gaze watching her every movement. Gaston had brought her some lobsters, and she grilled them carefully on the old-fashioned range, made a salad, and laid the table carefully with flowers, and fruit, and tall thin candles. She had just lit them, and was taking the lobsters from the stove, when the kitchen door was flung back. Laurence was standing there, a glass and a half empty whisky bottle in his hand. He had not changed from the clothes he had worn at the beach; he looked dishevelled and in need of a shave. He glowered at her, and she heard herself stammering.

'I thought I'd get dinner tonight,' she said. 'Marie-Christine . . .'

'I shan't be in for dinner,' he said abruptly. 'I'm going out.'

Disappointment welled up in her, but she bit back what she had been going to say.

'Oh, I'm sorry,' she said, as formally as she could. 'I didn't realise . . .'

'There's a lot of things you don't realise.' He kicked the door shut, and slammed the bottle of whisky violently down on the table. Involuntarily Katy backed away. His voice was slightly slurred; clearly he was drunk. His gaze took in the carefully laid table, the candles.

'What are you doing?' he asked, 'playing house? Is that it, Kate?'

'No,' she said quickly. 'It's just that I thought . . .'

'I don't give a damn what you thought!' He brought his arm up, and for a moment she thought he was going to smash everything on the floor, his face was so dark with anger.

'Games are for children, Kate. Don't try playing them with men . . .'

She could feel the tears of incomprehension and disappointment beginning to start in her eyes, and she moved towards the door.

'Where are you going?' he shouted at her, and when she made no answer, he laughed.

She hesitated in the doorway, frightened by his violence, yet reluctant to go.

'Please,' she said, 'I don't understand. I just . . .'

'Oh, get out,' he said roughly. 'Go to bed. Go to your room. What do I care? Go and write another sweet batch of letters to England, Kate—why don't you do that? God, I can't stand it . . .'

He raised his arm and hurled the glass he was holding the length of the kitchen. It smashed with a hideous suddenness on the stone floor. The colour drained from Katy's face. Without another word, she turned through the door, and ran up the stairs to her bedroom. She stood there, her breath coming in gasps, listening in the darkness. Almost immediately she heard the door slam, footsteps outside, and then the sound of his car's engine.

When she was sure he had gone, she went downstairs and cleaned up the mess in the kitchen. She felt sick, and ate nothing. In bed, she lay awake for a long time staring dry-eyed and tense at the ceiling, her mind coursing over the events of the day, trying to understand what had caused the outburst, how she could have angered him. She heard him return some time after midnight. Very late, she finally fell into a troubled and exhausted sleep.

Next day, in his study, he apologised shortly. He had been tired, he said, and worried about various things, and had drunk too much whisky. He hoped she would forget it. Then he behaved as he had before, reticently, formally, with a kind of automatic politeness and consideration. Neither of them referred to what had happened again.

CHAPTER SEVEN

ONE morning, about three weeks later, Katy came downstairs a little earlier than usual. She had slept well for once, her night mercifully undisturbed by dreams; she had been awake for what seemed an age, had breakfasted early. Looking into the study she saw that she was the first up for once—there was no sign of Laurence Martineau. Although she told herself it was foolish, she was feeling excited. It was the anniversary of the day she had arrived; he wouldn't remember, of course, but she had been keeping track of the days. It would be nice, she thought, if they could celebrate it in some way, and last night he had said they might go swimming . . . She wandered out into the garden, and on an impulse, picked some flowers, roses and honeysuckle, arranged them in a vase, and laid them on his desk. She went into the kitchen, and made some fresh coffee, strong, the way she knew he liked it, and set it on a tray with a pretty cloth, and some fine china cups. This, too, she took into the study, surprised that there was still no sign of him.

She might as well start work, she thought, so she brought in the letters from the hall, and was just beginning to open them when suddenly the telephone rang.

She reached automatically for the phone on her own desk, and then realised with surprise that it was the other phone, the direct line on Laurence Martineau's desk, which was shrilling. She hesitated. He had never actually made it clear whether she should answer that phone or not—the situation had never arisen . . . She let it ring perhaps four or five more times, thinking perhaps that he was upstairs, and would take the call there, but it continued pealing insistently. Finally, feeling that she had better answer, in case it was something important, she picked it up.

'Hallo?' she said. There was a moment's silence, then a woman's voice spoke.

'Hallo? Is Laurence there?'

Katy felt herself go suddenly cold, but keeping her voice even, she said:

'No, I'm afraid he isn't here at present. Could I take a message?'

'Who is that?' The voice was imperious, certainly English.

'This is his secretary,' Katy said. 'I'm sorry he's not here. If you'd just like to leave your . . '

'It doesn't matter,' the voice interrupted. Then there was a light, melodic laugh. 'I'm sure he'll know who it was . . .'

And whoever it was hung up. Katy stood there, rooted to the ground, feeling her cheeks flush with colour. It had been a beautiful voice, yet she hadn't liked it, hadn't liked the way the last remark had been made, confidently, yet also suggestively.

Fifteen minutes later she heard footsteps in the hall, the door was thrown wide.

'Kate!' Laurence Martineau strode in—he was wearing jodhpurs, and his hair was tousled. He greeted her affectionately. 'I'm late!' he said quickly. 'It was so infernally hot this morning, I thought I'd go for a ride, and went farther than I meant. Coffee! Just what I needed—you're a wonder. And flowers! Are we celebrating?'

'No,' she said flatly. 'I just thought they looked nice. I . . .' she hesitated, and something in her face stopped him short.

'What's the matter? Kate . . .' he came quickly across to her. 'What ever's happened? You look as if you'd seen a ghost!'

'No,' she said quickly. 'It's just that your phone went and I left it because I wasn't sure if I ought to answer it, but it went on and on, so I picked it up . . .'

'Who was it?' his tone was sharp.

She shook her head. 'I don't know,' she said, wondering why she suddenly felt so miserable. 'They wouldn't leave a name or message. It . . . it was a woman. She said you'd know who it was.'

'I see.' He turned away, so she could not see his face. There was an awkward silence. 'I think I'll just get some more hot water,' he said, 'the coffee's a little cold.'

He was away a long time, and when he came back his face looked tense, strung up, curiously elated. Katy felt pretty certain he'd telephoned whoever it was from the phone upstairs—

but so what if he had? she thought angrily to herself. It was nothing to do with her.

'Kate.' He hovered by the door, as if embarrassed. 'We'd planned to go swimming, hadn't we? Would you mind very much if we put it off until tomorrow? It's very humid today, anyway, and . . .'

'You have to go out,' she finished for him sullenly.

He gave her a keen look. 'Yes,' he said crisply, 'I'm afraid I do.'

There was a silence, and Katy wondered for a moment if he would give her an explanation, but of course he didn't.

'I'll leave now, if there are no problems,' he said finally. 'Then I shouldn't be too late back.'

'Oh, don't worry,' she said quickly, unable to keep the bitterness out of her voice. 'Do have a good time.'

She had half hoped that her tone might delay him, but of course it had the opposite effect. He simply left the room without a backward glance. When he had gone, she looked at the clock. It was half-past ten; the call had come at about nine-thirty. No wonder the woman had sounded so confident, she thought; she had him at her beck and call, that was obvious.

A wave of bitter anger swept over her, and she found it impossible to shake off. She tried to work, but could not concentrate. The voice she had heard plagued her. Who *was* it? Why did Laurence make these long departures? Well, the answer to that was pretty obvious too, she thought, and she had a moment's vision of that lean tanned body, lying back, sated, on a bed somewhere. Where—Cannes? Nice?

She slammed the papers back down on her desk, forcing the image out of her mind. What did it matter where it was, or with whom? Laurence wasn't the kind of man to lead a celibate existence, maybe he had dozens of women—if he did, it was none of her concern. Maybe if she herself had flirted a little, he might have responded. But no, she thought, she had never been able to take that kind of thing lightly. And besides, his attitude to her was as clear as crystal. As far as he was concerned, she was the substitute secretary, the young girl, *la jeune fille anglaise,* who just happened to be sharing his house for a month or two one summer. He'd never even paid her a compliment, she thought wretchedly; half the time he treated her as if she was invisible. He hadn't even mentioned when he wanted her to go back, and it would be just like him to announce suddenly that he'd booked her flight, that his secretary was returning in a couple of days.

A wild, uncontrollable panic surged within her, and she stood up abruptly. This was stupid, she told herself angrily. Ridiculous. Why was she so upset?

She gave up the attempt to work, for she knew she was too on edge. She tried to read; she went for a walk in the garden, but agitation possessed her. If she sat down she felt she must immediately get up again; if she looked at a book she saw no words, she just heard that repellent, melodious voice—*I'm sure he'll know who it was* ... As noon approached the weather grew more humid and thunderous. Thick sulphurous clouds blotted out the sun, and the air felt like steam on her skin. She went indoors, and sat in the kitchen for a while with Marie-Christine, watching her capable brown hands chopping and slicing vegetables, hardly hearing what she said. She refused lunch, for by then her head was aching and she felt sick. She went to her room and lay down on the cotton cover, but she could not get cool. She tossed and turned, and knew she would not sleep.

Dully, making an effort, she forced herself to take out her writing case. There were letters from Jane, and she should have answered them. She scanned their contents: Jane was ecstatic; she had a good modelling job at last, it seemed. She and Freddie were going on assignment somewhere glamorous, it wasn't yet decided where ... Katy wasn't the only one to get exciting invitations.

Katy sighed, and put the letters away. London seemed as remote as Moscow; Jane had no idea of the kind of life she had been living, and she hadn't the energy to write and disillusion her. What would she write if she wrote the truth? she thought bitterly, pushing her damp hair back from her forehead: 'Laurence Martineau has a mistress—or mistresses. He visits her—or them—almost every day, certainly every other. He looks through me like a pane of glass, and I'm being the perfect secretary . . .'

She was being really stupid now, she thought angrily. She put the writing case away, and stood at the window, looking out over the airless valley. For a moment she thought she heard the sound of a car; she tensed, but it was a tractor, and it passed on down to the village. She went downstairs again, as oppressed by the silence of the house as by the clammy heat of the weather. By the door in the hall hung one of Laurence's jackets. On a sudden instinct she buried her face in the cool folds of its linen. The scent of his skin hung on the jacket, and brought his presence back with an unbearable vividness.

Katy felt hot, miserable, near to tears. Whatever was the matter with her? she thought, pressing the material against her hot cheeks. It must be the weather, the unrelenting heat, the threat—Marie-Christine had said—of the mistral, the wind that presaged winter, and was said to bring madness. But it wasn't the mistral, it was something far more simple. And as she closed her eyes and pressed the linen against her skin, she acknowledged it to herself finally. Laurence wasn't there; she couldn't bear to imagine where he might be, and without him even a few hours were painfully, achingly, empty.

By the time he returned the sun was setting, but the temperature had hardly dropped. There was not the breath of a breeze. Katy was sitting on the terrace, sipping some wine. Her headache was worse; she felt ill with worry and temper. One glance at his face made her feel worse; he looked happier than he had for weeks. A stab of pain like a knife shot through her heart. She felt as if she had to know where he had been; if he didn't tell her, she would go mad . . .

Whistling gently, he fetched himself a drink, then came to sit beside her.

'I'm so sorry, Kate.' His hand brushed her arm in his usual absentminded way, and she felt as if she had been scalded. 'I'm late,' he said cheerfully, 'and you've been imprisoned here for hours in this awful weather—I hope it wasn't too boring.'

'Not at all.' She looked at him coldly. 'Did you have a good day?'

'Fine,' he said evenly.

'Did you go far?' She managed it casually enough, but the words nearly choked her.

'Far in what sense?'

She glanced at his face, and saw he was mocking her.

'How do you mean, in what sense?'

'Well now——' he stretched lazily in his chair. 'Far spiritually, physically, emotionally, geographically . . .?'

'Geographically, of course,' she snapped.

'Then I went as far as Cannes,' he said. 'Does that answer your question?'

It didn't, of course. Immediately a million other questions started up in her mind. Why Cannes? Who did he see there? She mustn't give him the satisfaction of seeing she cared, she thought desperately, as she saw the corners of his mouth curl. Damn him—he could have been to the North Pole, she told herself defiantly, for all it mattered to her!

'I wish *I* could go to Cannes,' she said, and she could hear the awful sulkiness in her own voice, but she couldn't stop it.

'Really? You want to go to Cannes? I can't imagine why anyone should.'

'Why not?' she said aggressively. 'It's supposed to be very beautiful, very glamorous. And besides, I've never been there.'

'Glamorous?' he laughed. 'Well, perhaps once—although that's a very misused and devalued word. But hardly now. It largely consists of over-priced hotels, lukewarm *paniers de champagne*, topless beaches, vulgar yachts and a whole street of soft-porn cinemas . . .'

'You go there,' she cut in accusingly. 'Why bother if it's so unpleasant?'

'I go because I have to,' he said curtly. 'It's not a place I would go to out of choice, believe me.'

'Well, I'd still like to go,' she said stubbornly. 'When I go back to England all my friends are going to ask if I went there. It's the first thing they'll ask.'

'How foolish of your friends,' he said. 'I wonder which of them you had in mind? Your colleagues who still work for the charming Mr Hunt, or your flatmate, or perhaps that rather earnest young man who plies you with red roses?'

'Bob is not earnest,' Katy said hotly, already regretting that she had started this wretched conversation.

'Oh, Bob? Is he not? I had the impression he was frightfully in earnest on the brief occasion I encountered him.'

'Being earnest and in earnest isn't the same thing,' she snapped.

'True,' he said. 'And your loyalty is touching. I couldn't possibly tell if he was earnest. In earnest, however—yes, I would say he was that.'

'Well, it doesn't matter anyway.' Katy now felt desperate to channel the whole conversation elsewhere.

'Doesn't it?' he said. 'No, perhaps it doesn't. Still——' and. he got up and wandered to the edge of the terrace so he could look out over the valley. 'It would be a pity to disappoint your friends, wouldn't it, Kate? I mean, clearly your return to England is uppermost in your thoughts, and I'd hate to rob you of the opportunity of telling your—friends—about Cannes. That would be churlish of me, don't you think? If you want to see the bright lights perhaps I should take you. In fact——' and he turned to face her, with that odd infuriating mocking smile on his face, 'I will take you. We shall go to-morrow. We'll go for dinner. You can wear your most beautiful dress, and I shall put on the sort of clothes considered suitable for such expeditions, and we'll go. Now, will that suit you?'

'Don't be silly,' she said. 'You hate the place—what's the point in going?'

'Who knows?' he shrugged. 'There might be a point—we can go, and we can see what happens.'

Katy stared at him. His manner was very odd. She suspected him of mocking her, and wouldn't altogether have blamed him. But there was no mockery in his face; he looked, she thought suddenly, like a gambler who had just staked all his chips on one throw; he looked exhilarated by daring—and yet what was daring about an expedition for dinner in Cannes?

'Lukewarm *paniers de champagne*?' she said.

'Certainly. And rude waiters, and crowded restaurants, and oysters and lobsters and caviare. Plunging necklines and famous faces and *paparazzi*.' He laughed. 'Come on, Kate, say yes—enough of living like hermits!'

And suddenly she laughed too, caught up in his exhilaration, excited in spite of herself. It *would* be fun, she thought, dressing up a little, and driving off into the night along the necklace of bright lights of the Côte d'Azur. It would be fun to stop being a secretary for a few hours, and pretend she was just a girl, going out to dinner with this man . . .

'Yes,' she said. 'Yes, let's! It doesn't matter if it's awful, does it? I'm sure if you say it is, then it is—but we could laugh at it together, warm champagne and *paparazzi* and all.'

'Could we?' he said, and she was aware that his mood had changed again, for the words were said seriously. He gave her a long, still look, and her eyes faltered under that direct gaze. 'Could we do that, do you think? Well, if we could then it might be worthwhile. Now—shall we go inside and have dinner? Here, take your jacket, it's getting cold.'

As it happened, it wasn't, Katy thought, for although the sun was now down, it still felt hot and airless even outside. But Laurence came across, took her hand, and gently wrapped her jacket around her shoulders. His hands brushed the back of her neck, and for a moment she felt a wild desire to reach up and hold them there. They paused, and there was a moment's silence. In that moment Katy suddenly knew—and there was no arguing—why she had been so miserable that afternoon.

That was what she wanted. She wanted him to be there, but more than that she wanted him to touch her. She wanted it passionately with every cell of her body. Indeed, for the first time in her life, her body spoke, and there was no dismissing its language. It ached to be touched by this man; every cell, every organ, every pore of her skin ached for the alchemy of his touch. Suddenly the memory of that night by the canal in London—that night that now seemed such ages before—came back again to her sharply. The memory of that sudden harsh kiss arced through her body like a current, and she wanted it again, fiercely; she craved it. She half-turned, and she knew what she felt must be naked on her face. But if Laurence saw it he made no sign. He drew back swiftly; something Katy had been about to say died on her lips, and she followed him inside to eat dinner.

Katy woke the next day early. She had had that dream again, she realised, as she lay back on the pillows. The dream about Camilla—it must have been the third or fourth time. But today, even the memory of that couldn't depress her. She felt already a sense of excitement and exhilaration. She jumped out of bed, threw back the shutters, ran a deep bath, and sang while she bathed. She looked through the wardrobe, pretending to select a dress for that evening, but she already knew what she would wear—one of the new dresses she had bought, one in which Laurence hadn't yet seen her. She brought it out and laid it gently on the bed, her hands smoothing its silky folds. It was beautiful she thought; and so it should have been, her mind added wryly, remembering the price tag.

It was the most expensive dress she had ever possesed; also the most daring. It was black, of silk chiffon, cut with deceptive simplicity. At the back, it plunged to the waist, at the front it curved softly over her breasts. All that held it up was two fine straps of diamanté. She didn't care—she knew it looked good against the apricot flow of her skin, against the chestnut fall of her hair—and it made her feel good too, slightly wicked, sophisticated, like a heroine in a thirties movie.

She was sick of looking too thin, too boyish, she thought. She might not look like the film stars Laurence Martineau was used to even in this, but at least she would look less like a schoolgirl than usual. She would wash her hair, she planned, make an effort with her make-up for once. She would look thirty years old and unbelievably soignée, and Mr Laurence Martineau would be—well, what would he be? Katy didn't let herself answer that question. But at least he might notice her, she thought, at least he might stop treating her as if she were invisible. Maybe he would stop treating her like a girl, and realise she was a woman. Her hands shook slightly as she replaced the dress carefully in the wardrobe.

She had breakfast in her room as usual, but could hardly eat she felt so excited. She tried to calm herself down—after all, they were only going out to dinner, and he was only being kind in taking her; it was an indulgence on his part, just another aspect of his patient hospitality. He was probably bored by the whole idea, she thought, feeling suddenly panicky. After all, he hated Cannes—he'd made that plain enough. They were only going because she had made a spoilt scene; he no doubt despised her for wanting to go there in the first place. But all this only made her more nervous, and she felt trapped in a web of feelings she didn't understand—didn't want to question too closely. She made a deliberate effort to shut her mind down. She would go and work; she would forget about the evening.

When she reached the study, Laurence Martineau was already there. The morning's pile of mail was already in its place on her desk, and he was seated at his looking idly at some papers.

'You have a letter,' he said coolly. 'From one of your friends in London.' There was a slight edge in his voice, and her eyes fell on an airmail envelope neatly placed on the top of the pile. Even at that distance, she could recognise the handwriting.

She sat down without comment, and picked up the envelope. It was from Bob; his name and address were on the back of the envelope, written in his small neat hand. Laurence usually brought the mail in each morning; she had no doubt he had read the inscription—Bob Parrish, St James's Hospital, London W1. Katy placed the letter calmly on one side, unopened.

'Aren't you going to read it?'

This time there was no mistaking the edge in his voice, and it irritated her. What had he got against Bob? she thought. He had only glimpsed him once, but whenever he referred to him, it was with hostility.

'I'll read it later.'

'Come, come, Katharine. It's from an old friend. I think you ought to read it, then we can get on with our work. There's a lot to do this morning.'

'Very well.'

She sighed, and reached for the paper-knife. She did quite want to read it. She had not heard from Bob since she left London, and such a long silence was unlike him.

She slid the letter out from the envelope, noting that it seemed unusually long. Bob always wrote if either of them were away, but his letters were almost always short—he worked so hard, such long hours, he had little time for correspondence . . . her eyes scanned the first page quickly, aware that Laurence was watching her intently, so intently she could hardly concentrate on what she was reading. It was an odd letter, Katy thought, it sounded curiously stiff and stilted . . . She turned the page, and involuntarily caught her breath.

Laurence leaned forward. She read on to the end, folded the letter up, and put it back in its envelope, trying to keep her face quite expressionless.

'Good news?'

'Yes, I suppose it is,' she said slowly.

'All well in London?'

'Yes,' she said, keeping her eyes firmly fixed on her desk. 'It's from Bob Parrish. You know—you saw him that time.

The young man with the red roses.' Which you know already, she thought rebelliously. He didn't even bother to look surprised, she noted.

'Ah yes, the earnest young man.'

Silence.

'And is he well? Missing you, no doubt?'

'Hardly at all,' she said coldly. 'He's getting married, as a matter of fact. It's all happened rather swiftly. He's marrying one of the nurses at his hospital—Mandy. I've met her once or twice.'

She kept her eyes firmly averted from his face, so she didn't see his reaction. Nor did she want him to see hers. She felt suddenly confused, and a little shaken. Bob—and Mandy. And she remembered them both sitting side by side on the sofa in the sitting-room the evening Mandy had first dropped in. The first time they had met; Mandy had visibly worshipped Bob, and Katy had assumed Bob had found her transparent adoration as tiresome as she had done. She had almost forgotten her, though Bob mentioned her from time to time. They worked in the same ward . . .

Did she mind? She wasn't sure. She had looked on Bob for so long as her property, the eternal suitor, the would-be lover who would never let her down. And now this! And to Mandy of all people—plump, goodnatured Mandy, whom she had always liked but whom she had felt was a little ridiculous.

Serves you right, Katharine Sutcliffe, she told herself. It was you who dismissed all thoughts of a rival, you who was smug, you who thought you'd have Bob Parrish at your beck and call for as long as you wanted him. And she laughed, though she felt close to tears. She hadn't loved Bob, she knew that now, but how would her life be, without the man who had always been her safety net?

'Katharine.'

Laurence got up. He came across to her desk, and put his arm around her shoulders. It was a fatherly gesture, she thought, and instinctively she flinched, though her whole body burned at that gentle touch.

'I'm sorry,' he said gently. 'If you're upset . . . we can leave the work this morning if you would prefer . . .'

'Upset?' Katy looked at him angrily. 'Why should I be upset? I'm extremely pleased for them.'

'You don't look exactly pleased,' he said. 'Come on, Katharine, we know each other well enough now, surely. You don't need to hide your feelings from me.'

'Don't I?' she said rather wildly. 'It seems to me that I never do anything else.'

She looked up at him, aware that her face was flushed, and tears were starting in her eyes—not tears for Bob Parrish, but Laurence would never know that. He looked puzzled, genuinely anxious, she thought with surprise. He could be so harsh that his moments of gentleness always alarmed her.

'Katharine,' he said slowly, 'I know we haven't talked about this—I thought you preferred not to. But I know that you felt—felt something for this man. You're upset now, it's obvious. Don't try to hide feelings like that, it's only misplaced pride that makes one do it, you know. Whatever has happened, if you—cared for him—it's better to say so. If you love someone you should never hide it. You should shout it from the rooftops—even if it all goes wrong. Even if you feel you're making a fool of yourself. Love isn't something—shouldn't be something—that's hidden . . .'

'Oh, isn't it?' she almost shouted at him, interrupting him. 'You make it all sound so simple, don't you? What do you know about it? Stop preaching at me—stop treating me like a child! You're not my father!'

She saw his face go white, as if she had hit him, and he instantly drew back.

'I'm sorry, Katharine,' he said stiffly. 'Please believe me, I don't think of you in that way. But I am much older than you, and I just thought that perhaps——'

'You're doing it again,' she cried impulsively, aware that the tears were now spilling over. 'You treat me like a child. I'm not a child, I'm a woman. You don't understand my feelings at all. Not at all!'

'Katharine, please.' She had turned away from him, and she felt his arms come gently round her. All she wanted to do was to turn and be enveloped in those arms, but she kept her body rigid and her face averted though it took every ounce of her will power to do so.

'These feelings will pass,' he said. 'Believe me, they will. It may seem the end of the world now. But it isn't. You're young, you're beautiful. There will be other men who aren't so foolish—who aren't like Parrish——'

She noticed he seemed hardly able to make himself speak Bob's name. 'Katharine, believe me, there will be someone else, someone who would rather die than let you escape from him. Wait for that, Katharine. It's worth waiting for.'

'I don't want some other man,' she cried. 'I want——' and she just managed to stop herself. But her whole mind and body sang the words in her head, although her mouth did not speak them. *I want you, Laurence Martineau*, she thought, *I want you*.

'You want *him*?' The contempt in his voice was naked, and he gestured towards the letter.

'For God's sake,' she snapped, turning to him, her pain and confusion soaring into sudden and genuine anger, 'I *don't* want him. I've never wanted him. Can't you understand that? He wanted *me*; my mother pushed it, his mother pushed it. The whole bloody village pushed it. The only thing wrong was that *I* didn't want it. I liked Bob, and I used him, I leant on him. But I never loved him, never. And I wouldn't marry him. He asked me and I said no, and I meant it. So nothing has changed, has it?'

She could hear her own voice rising, and she realised she must sound stupid and hysterical, but she didn't care any longer.

'Kate.' His face was a few inches from her own, and his eyes searched hers. She could hear a strange catch in his voice as he said her name—his name for her, the first time he had used it for days.

'Kate, is that true—you're not pretending?'

'Of course it's true,' she cried. 'You're so bloody blind. Can't you see—it's obvious, isn't it? I'm no actress!'

'Don't swear, Kate,' he said gently. 'That's twice now, and it doesn't become you.'

Her lips parted to say something—anything—some insult, but the words were never uttered. Very gently, very firmly, he pulled her into his arms; they tightened around her, her breath caught and the room spun. Slowly, deliberately, he bent his head and kissed her full on the lips. It was a long kiss—longer than the kiss that first night in London, longer than eternity itself, for time seemed to stop. Her heart felt as if it had ceased beating, her eyes closed, her mind ceased its painful whirling, its interior arguments, evasions and lies. She heard nothing—not the sounds of the country outside the window, not the ticking of the clock. The world disappeared; there was no world, no room, no time, just his mouth upon hers, his body against hers, his skin against hers.

She pressed herself passionately against him, all those weeks of wanting this touch suddenly unleashed and possessing her. Her lips parted, and she felt his breath quicken, his kiss grew rougher. His hands moved over her body, as she clung to him, pressing her tighter to him, her thighs against his. He caressed her waist, her back, her neck, her breasts, and she felt them swell and harden against him, and still the kiss went on, as if he would suck the soul forth from her body.

After a long, long while he drew back a little, he rained kisses on her face, her eyes, her hair, then he pressed her head down into the crook of his shoulder and held her there, cradled in his arms, gently stroking the back of her neck, and running his fingers through the long strands of her hair.

She was shaking all over, her body caught in an uncontrollable trembling; her blood pounded in her head, her whole body surged with desire for him. She would have done anything for him then, whatever he wanted, and she knew with a blind certainty what he wanted, for she could feel it in every line of his body. She cared for nothing then, no morality, no codes of behaviour, no propriety, none of the old sad caveats about not making yourself cheap—such concepts were worlds away from that room and that moment, they belonged to another woman on another planet. All caution gone, she clung to him, and she knew he sensed her want, and knew that she sensed his, for he tried to calm himself and to calm her, holding her with an infinite gentleness, until the sharp edge of the passion subsided and ebbed, to be replaced with a glorious calm, a glorious peace, a glorious happiness, a certainty of soul Katy had never known in her life.

Neither of them could speak, she realised, but every touch of his hands, however gentle, brought forth little inarticulate cries from her throat, cries that seemed to come from deep inside her, which made him catch his breath. His mouth sought hers again with a sharp renewed urgency.

At last, with great deliberateness, he put her from him, held her tight by the hands, but held her at arm's length, and looked searchingly into her face.

'My dearest Kate,' he said, and his voice was roughened, changed, quite unlike the voice she knew and had heard in her sleep each night since she came there.

She couldn't say anything, not even his name, not a word. *I love you*, her heart sang, *I love you*. But her throat felt choked and she was silent.

'Four weeks,' he said slowly. 'Four weeks and one day and God knows how many hours since I last kissed you, and not a minute of those has gone past without my wanting to touch you, to hold you. Did you know that, Kate?' She shook her head wordlessly.

'Do you know what it cost me not to touch you, not to kiss you? I think you must have bewitched me, Kate. Walking and sleeping—having you in my dreams and then losing you each morning. In my whole life I've never . . .'

She found her voice.

'I love you!' she cried. But the words came out all wrong, scarcely audible, flat, childish—and she felt stupid at once. What an idiot he would think her—so inexperienced. One kiss and she offered him her heart.

And indeed she saw his face change instantly. The guarded look came back into his eyes; he dropped his gaze, and turned away from her. She felt as if the whole world were crashing to the ground at her feet.

'Dear Kate, don't,' he said quietly.

And he kissed her very gently on the forehead, as if he were comforting a child.

By the time the evening came she was in a turmoil, a fever. She painted her face as expertly as she could, but her hands were shaking as she wielded the brushes. She put on the black dress and stood for a long while in front of the glass. A stranger looked back at her; in place of a thin, somewhat tomboyish girl, stood a slender woman. The dress snaked over the curves of her body; the mounds of her breasts rose tantalisingly above the dipped neckline; the long line of her back to the waist and just below was exposed. Her thick hair fell in shiny waves over smooth tanned skin; her cheeks were slightly flushed; her eyes enormous, dark, bright—as if she had taken some drug. What was the drug that made the pupils huge and dilated? Belladonna, that was it. Her lips were slightly parted, shiny, painted scarlet. *Belladonna*. She looked slightly predatory, this woman, Katy thought; she didn't quite like her, hardly recognised her.

She looked at the apparently poised apparition in the glass, and her mind raced, a helter-skelter of contrary thoughts and emotions. Memories of the day flashed through her brain. She thought of what he had said—*if you love someone, Kate, you should shout it from the rooftops*. Well, she virtually had, she thought bitterly, and much good it had done her.

The events of the past day all jumbled in her mind—she didn't know how she had got through the hours until the evening. He had kissed her, she thought. He had wanted her— she knew it, and he had said so. But he didn't love her—that was transparently clear. He was an honest man, she thought. Maybe he was worried at being disloyal to his mistress. Anyway, he hadn't touched her again that day, and she thought she knew why. He didn't want to hurt her, and once she had blurted out those fatal words—oh, *why* hadn't she kept her mouth shut?—he'd realised that for her it wasn't just a physical attraction as it was for him. She had put a demand on him which he couldn't fulfil, and so, kindly, considerately, he was disentangling himself. He was not a heartbreaker, she thought, at least, not intentionally.

But still—and she gazed at the strange woman in the glass— he had wanted her. She wanted him to want her again, even if he didn't care for her. That was better than nothing, she thought defiantly. She would *make* him want her; damn his control, and damn his reticence, and damn that wretched woman who had telephoned. She had played the role of secretary long enough, she thought—why shouldn't she play the role of seductress? After all, she had nothing to lose— did she? *You have everything to lose*, said a voice in her mind. *It's worth the risk*, said the strange dark apparition in the glass.

So she waited until she heard him in the hall below, and he called up to her. Then she made an entrance. She came down the stairs slowly, giving him plenty of time to take in this new woman. And she was rewarded. He froze, and she saw his face register surprise, admiration, desire. She felt triumphant. But she wasn't an actress, and she hadn't thought beyond that first entrance, with the result that by the time she had reached the bottom of the stairs, he was in command of himself again, and she couldn't think what to do next. She tried to think of something light and witty to say, and her mind went blank. To her fury, she saw him suppress a smile that tugged at the corners of his mouth.

'You look very beautiful, Kate,' he said, with a noxiously assured gallantry. 'You've effected an extraordinary transformation.'

'Not so extraordinary, surely, Laurence?' she said, and brushed her hand against his cheek in what was meant to be a sophisticated gesture of flirtation. Neither words nor gesture quite worked. They were tremulous and forced, but then it had cost her a great effort to say his name so familiarly.

'Don't you think you should take a coat?' he asked gravely, eyeing her bared back, shoulders, breasts, arms in a way which made her feel acutely selfconscious. She didn't have a suitable coat—only an old woollen one, and she had no intention of spoiling the effect of the dress by putting that on.

'No, no,' she said gaily, 'it's frightfully hot still. I don't need one.'

'The weather's going to change,' he told her. 'The mistral won't hold off much longer—it might be very cold by the time we get back.'

'Then you'll give me your jacket, won't you?' she said sweetly. And she teetered out to the car somewhat unsurely on her five-inch spiky heels.

She didn't manage much better in the car, she thought. She tried hard, but even to her own ears her dialogue sounded dreadfully stale, dredged up from some tired old movie. But if Laurence noticed her efforts (and their lack of success), he made no comment, and gradually she relaxed a little. It wasn't quite so easy to be a siren as she had imagined, she thought wryly, and as time passed, and they still drove on through the silent countryside on the dark winding roads that led down to the coast, the desire to play-act gradually left her. She felt so happy sitting there in that dark space with that man that she wanted the journey to go on for ever. She no longer wanted to get to Cannes, to see bright lights, hear music, encounter people. She wanted them to stay locked up in that car, that night, for ever.

But after perhaps half an hour they saw the lights of the autoroute ahead of them. The Lagonda accelerated up on to it, and Katy could see ahead of them a pool of glittering lights under the dark hills. She drew in her breath. It was Cannes.

CHAPTER EIGHT

THEY drove along the famous Boulevard de la Croisette, and tall white buildings, palm trees, the harbour, yachts all lit up, flashed past them. Laurence pulled up outside a huge white palace of a building, with a terrace in front of it crowded with people.

'The Carlton,' he said. 'We could have gone to the Reine Pédauque, which has better food, I think. But you've come to see Cannes, so you'd better see the Carlton.'

Katy had heard of it, of course. It was one of the most celebrated hotels in France—the place where all the stars stayed during the annual Film Festival. She felt nervous, and Laurence seemed to sense it, because he smiled at her encouragingly, and pressed her hand.

'Come on,' he said. 'It *is* an experience, if nothing else. It's pure theatre, you'll see—princes, gamblers, producers, starlets, merchants, and dreamers, all talking with extreme animation to each other, and looking over their shoulder to see if someone more important has just come into the room. You'll enjoy it. Come on, Kate, you promised we could laugh at it together.'

They had been closeted away for so many weeks now at La Bayardière that Katy had almost forgotten what happened when Laurence Martineau appeared in public—let alone a place like the Carlton. As they crossed the terrace to the dining room, she heard the conversation lull, was conscious that all heads turned in their direction.

'Good God, it's Laurence Martineau!' exclaimed a woman as they passed.

He cut through the stir he caused like a scythe through corn, holding tight to her arm and propelling her forward.

The maître d'hôtel cringed when he saw them, there was no other word. His gloved palms came together, his body doubled up in an attitude of obeisance. 'Monsieur Martineau—*quel plaisir*! Mademoiselle . . .'

He ushered them into the huge room which blazed with light from the vast crystal chandeliers overhead. Katy had a fleeting impression of glitter and opulence, diamonds and silks, air rich with scent and cigar smoke, and again the babble of conversation stilled, all heads turned as the head waiter escorted them to their table.

They were in a corner, shielded somewhat by tall red velvet banquettes, but still open to stares—and there were plenty of them—on their flank. The maître d'hôtel made a discreet gesture to a hovering waiter.

'*Champagne, vite, pour* Monsieur Martineau.'

The man hastened away, and within seconds an ice bucket appeared, and the maître d'hôtel himself opened the champagne bottle.

'Bollinger '75, Monsieur Martineau,' he made a little bow. '*Avec nos compliments.*'

He backed away, and Laurence gave Katy a sidelong glance.

'It's not lukewarm,' she commented.

'No.' He tasted it. 'It's very good. I have the feeling, how-ever, that we may not be going to enjoy a very intimate supper.'

Katy sipped the champagne from a long fluted glass, and looked around her. Even without drinking she felt a little in-toxicated. Never in her life had she been in such a place. Music was playing in an adjoining room. All around them was the glitter of crystal and silver on damask. The room was filled with beautiful women wearing the kind of clothes and the kind of jewellery she had glimpsed only in the pages of magazines. She stared at them, fascinated, and saw them stare back, and wondered if she passed muster in such an assembly. She became aware that Laurence was watching her, with that same lazy detachment in his eyes.

'You like it?'

'Well, I don't *not* like it,' she said. 'I've never been anywhere like it in my life.'

'So you feel you're seeing the world? Which, as I remember, you were rather anxious to do.'

Again she heard that slight edge in his voice, but she wasn't ready to heed the warning. Why should she? She was enjoying herself. As she became conscious that not just the women but also the men at some of the surrounding tables were staring in her direction, she suddenly felt new confidence in her decided role of siren. She gave him what she profoundly hoped was a slow, smouldering smile, and she leaned forward a little so that the mounds of her breasts spilled a little more obviously over the black silk chiffon.

'I'm not seeing the world,' she said (as huskily as she could). 'I'm seeing your world. This is part of it, surely.'

'Not the part I prefer,' he said coldly, but all the same she saw his eyes lower, saw him note—not entirely indifferently—the alteration in the neckline of her dress.

She drained her glass of champagne, and before she had put the glass down, a tail-coated waiter had expertly refilled it.

The menus were brought, pages of French, handwritten in spiky writing, and with relief she let Laurence take charge. She heard him order things she had never eaten, things whose names she didn't even recognise—*loup flambé, mousseline de rascasse, daurade au plat,* a *carré d'agneau Arlésienne.* Bottles of wine kept appearing—all handled by the waiters with extreme reverence.

'You like it?' He looked at her enquiringly.

'It's like nectar and ambrosia,' she said. 'I feel as if I were having dinner on Mount Olympus.'

'But you're dining with a man, not a god, Kate,' he said gently.

'I'm not so sure,' she said flirtatiously, sipping more wine. 'After all, look at the way these people treat you. You're the nearest thing we have in the modern world to a god—you're a film star, and your films make you immortal.'

'Those films?' he snorted. 'They're more likely to consign me to oblivion.'

'No, they won't,' she said. 'People will be watching them years from now—long after both of us are dead and gone . . .'

'Not a prospect that particularly pleases me,' he said.

'Oh, why do you have to be so grim about it all?' she sighed. 'Aren't you what everyone wants to be—rich, and famous and successful?'

She put her hand on his arm, and though she could see the expression on his face, she refused to allow it to daunt her.

'You think those things are important, Kate?'

She could hear a certain danger in his voice that she recognised, but she wasn't going to let it stop her. She sipped more wine, the glass was refilled; she felt heady and reckless—ready to risk saying anything.

'If they're not important, what is?'

He looked at her again, and there was such pain and desperation in his face that she almost stopped, dropped the whole ridiculous masquerade, but by then the wine was taking effect, and she didn't.

'Another of your questions,' he said. 'I'll answer it with one of my own. What matters to you, Kate? Sometimes I wonder.'

'Matters to me?' she smiled. 'Lots of things matter to me.'

'Such as?'

'Well——' She paused. She knew what mattered to her, only too well, she thought, but after this morning she had no intention of repeating her mistake, no intention of telling him. 'Enjoying oneself. Evenings like this—going to a wonderful place and eating wonderful food, drinking lovely wine. Having a delectable man to flirt with, and having lots of people watch me do it. Why not? That's fun at least,' she said, seeing his ominous expression. 'Why worry about more serious things—none of them matter anyway.'

'What about your work?' His tone was level, but she had the distinct impression he was controlling his temper with difficulty. So what? she thought. Let him be angry—it's a reaction, I don't care.

'Work? It occupies one's time. It pays the rent,' she said flippantly.

'And marriage?'

That one word, on his lips, sent a sliver of ice through her heart, but she was not going to be stopped now.

'Marriage?' she said, and she put as much scorn into her voice as she could muster. 'Oh, I think that's an outworn convention, don't you? It seems to me such an impractical invention. I mean, it ignores the realities, doesn't it?'

She hesitated, and sipped more wine to give herself courage. She had had this argument before once, with Jane as it happened. Then Katy had taken the opposite stance, but she wasn't going to do that now. What had been Jane's argument? She wrinkled her brow; it was coming back to her.

'The realities?'

'Yes,' she said. 'It . . . it seems to me to be foolish to hang on to impossible beliefs. You know—till death us do part and all that. After all, men have always recognised their need to be free, to have love affairs. For the first time now women are able to acknowledge that they feel the same way . . .'

Her voice died away. He was looking at her stonily, and the contempt in his eyes terrified her. But the wine was taking effect, and she couldn't stop.

'In any case,' she went on, trying to sound bright and artificial, 'I don't have a great deal of experience in the matter, do I? You've been married; I haven't. You should be telling me what it's like, not listening to my untried opinions. What is it like, Laurence? After all, I don't know.'

'I can only speak for myself,' he said quietly. 'In my case, it was a living hell.'

Whatever Katy had been going to say next, and she had no idea what it was, for her mind was whirling, it died on her lips. There was no mistaking the pain and the cold anger of his words. She felt the blood rush to her cheeks, and she turned away, confused and deeply ashamed of herself.

Out of the corner of her eye she saw Laurence nod to the waiter; in a second her glass had been refilled. She didn't touch it. She must stop this, the thought desperately, it was all going wrong. She'd drunk far too much, too fast . . . perhaps if she had some black coffee . . .

But before she could ask for any, he leaned back against the banquette, draping his arm across it and behind her, the classic preliminary, she realised in horror, to the fondling grasp around the shoulders. What was happening? Within a moment she knew. The black-jacketed arm slid down the banquette and around her bare shoulders. But it didn't stop there. His long fingers caressed her bared back and shoulders proprietorially. Katy tensed, arousal and outrage fought within her. She swung round to face him, to find him looking at her with an expression that was unmistakable. It was the totally confident, patronising smile of the man who is about to make a pass at a woman and fears no rebuttal. She stared at him in disbelief, mesmerised in spite of herself. It was as if he had suddenly thrown a switch, and the full power of his sexuality and physical magnetism hit her like a wave.

'Please, don't,' she faltered. 'Laurence, please . . .'

He ignored her. He let his arm slide farther down, towards her breast, and she froze, paralysed with shame, aware that at the next table conversation had come to a complete halt and everyone was looking in their direction. He smiled a long, slow mocking smile.

'Oh, come on, Katharine,' he said lazily. 'Don't play the virtuous little virgin with me. I see I was wrong about you before—quite wrong. Relax, have some more wine. As you say, we're here to enjoy ourselves, aren't we? Why be coy about it?'

She attempted to shrug him off, but he just held her more tightly, his fingers biting painfully into her skin.

'Come on,' he said. 'You were just giving a very good impression of a good-time girl. Don't spoil it now, my dear.'

She was trembling all over, and she knew he could feel it, but it seemed only to add to his enjoyment. Suddenly she felt sick and faint. His dark impenetrable face was unreadable as she looked at him pleadingly. Was he acting, just as she had been? she thought. Or was that how he really felt, had he just been waiting for the right sort of encouragement?

'Please,' she said, keeping her voice to a whisper. 'Please, Laurence, don't humiliate me. I didn't mean . . .'

He smiled dazzlingly, and bent his head so that he could kiss her neck. At the touch of his lips a shudder went through her whole body. His mouth was close to her ear.

'Come on, Katharine,' he said softly, 'I warned you once before, didn't I? You can play games with boys, but don't try them with men.'

'I wasn't playing games,' she lied desperately.

'All the better.'

'Laurence—Mr Martineau—please . . . I—I feel faint. I'd like some coffee.'

He laughed sarcastically, and let her go as suddenly as he had held her. 'Waiter!' The man was at the table in a second. 'We'd like some coffee please, and some brandy . . .'

'No,' Katy said weakly. 'Not brandy. Just some coffee. I . . .'

'I've ordered it now.' Again the dazzling icy smile. 'Have some. Relax, Katharine. We've a long, long night ahead of us.'

All she could think of now was getting out of the room, if only for a moment. She rose awkwardly to her feet, peering across the haze of candles, smoke, indistinct faces . . . There must be a cloakroom, she thought desperately.

'Will you excuse me?' she muttered.

'But of course. Don't be long, darling.'

He used the endearment like a whip; she didn't hesitate. She brushed past the table, and hastened across the room, averting her eyes from the stares.

She found the cloakroom on the far side, and went in, seeing with relief that it was empty except for an attendant. Quickly she ran some cold water in the basin, and splashed her face; she held her wrists under the cold tap. The woman watched her curiously.

'*Vous êtes malade, madame? Voulez-vous une aspirine?*'

'*Non, merci,*' she said quickly. '*J'ai chaud, c'est tout . . .*'

The woman nodded sagely. '*Bien sûr,*' she said. '*Le mistral, vous savez . . .*'

With shaking hands Katy re-applied some make-up. She powdered her nose, put on some more lipstick, combed her hair. Gradually she began to feel calmer. It was all her fault, she thought. She'd go straight back and explain, surely he'd understand. A voice cut through her reverie.

'Well, well, well. Look who's saved me a phone call!'

She swung round, and stared in disbelief. Leaning against the door, watching her, was Jane. For a moment Katy hardly recognised her, she looked so amazingly elegant; the strawberry dye had been changed, and now her face was surrounded by a halo of platinum blonde curls. Jane gave a broad grin, and came across and hugged her, then held her at arm's length.

'Well!' she exclaimed. 'Who'd have thought it! We've both effected a transformation. I know they say that sooner or later you always run into someone you know at the Carlton, but this is ridiculous!'

'Jane!' she found her voice. 'Whatever are you doing here?'

Jane grinned, and pulled out her compact.

'I know you don't answer letters these days,' she said wryly, 'but I did write and tell you I'd got a modelling job at last, didn't I? Well, guess where it turned out to be? The good old Côte d'Azur! I've been on the beach with Freddie for days—Pucci pyjamas, slinky swimsuits, the lot! We're due back to-morrow, worse luck, and I was going to ring you before I left. As I say, you saved me that phone call. Like my tan?' She held out her long thin arms for inspection, and Katy smiled.

'Very impressive,' she said. She was beginning to feel better.

Jane gave her a sideways look.

'You don't look too bad yourself,' she commented drily. 'A little mauled, but then judging from what was going on earlier, I'm not surprised!'

'What?' Katy followed her eyes and looked down at her

shoulder The red marks left by Laurence Martineau's fingers stood out clearly on her smooth skin. She blushed crimson.

'Freddie and I had a grandstand view, love.' Jane looked at her intently. 'I was going to come across to your table, but the scene looked a bit heavy, so . . .'

'Yes, well,' Katy cut her off. 'It was just a misunderstanding.'

Jane's eyes widened mockingly.

'You don't say? I was a bit surprised, it's true. So were the people we're with. An old friend—or enemy—of yours, as it happens. Freddie's worked with him in the past, and we ran into him on the beach yesterday. He's paying, otherwise we wouldn't be here tonight. Even *Vogue* expenses don't run to the Carlton.'

Katy stared at her.

'Someone I know? I don't understand . . .'

Jane put her compact back in her bag. Her face looked suddenly serious. 'I'll give you a clue,' she said. 'He was *most* entertained by the *drame* at your table. "Little Miss Iceberg", he calls you . . .'

'Dick Hunt?'

'The one and only.'

Katy froze.

'It can't be,' she said quickly. 'Here, in Cannes? But why should . . .'

'Don't ask me,' Jane interrupted. 'I don't know and I don't want to. Frankly, I think he's a helluva pain, but he's a useful contact for Freddie, so I had to come tonight. He was just about to go across to your table, as it happens, which is why I excused myself and slipped in here. I thought you might be grateful for the warning.'

'Oh no!' Katy turned hurriedly for the door. She'd better get back, she thought. God knew what would happen if Dick Hunt encountered Laurence in the mood he'd been in earlier. A repetition of the scene at Angelo's would be ghastly . . .

'Hey, hang on!' Jane came after her. 'Just a second, Katy. There's something else . . .'

'Tell me back at the table,' Katy called over her shoulder. 'You'd better come over, it might help!'

She hastened across the brilliantly lit room, not even looking back to see if Jane was following her. Their table was obscured from her view by the high velvet banquettes, and for a moment she half hoped Dick Hunt had changed his mind. If he had, she could warn Laurence, she'd have the perfect excuse to leave . . .

But her hopes were forestalled. As she reached their table, she stopped short. The waiters had brought some extra chairs. Seated expansively on one of them, sweating heavily, and encased in a dinner jacket several sizes too tight, was Dick Hunt. But he wasn't alone. On the banquette, next to Laurence, was a woman. Katy stopped dead in her tracks. She was tall, and exquisitely dressed, with long pale hair falling loosely over her shoulders. Her eyes were fixed on Katy and her expression was a strange mixture of hurt, and gentle welcome. She looked years younger than Katy would have expected, and much more beautiful than in photographs, but Katy recognised her instantly. As she reached the table, and Dick Hunt rose clumsily to his feet, the woman held out a long slender hand.

'Hallo,' she said shyly, melodiously, her soft voice hardly more than a whisper. 'We haven't met, I think. I'm Camilla Drew.'

Katy stared, unable to speak. Something plucked at her memory, but she couldn't quite place it in the confusion and shock. Had she met Camilla Drew before? But no, of course, that was impossible. She would have remembered—it was not a face you forgot. Perhaps it was the memory of seeing her act, all those years before . . .

Before she could speak, Dick Hunt had drawn her to him, and planted a blubbery kiss on her cheek.

'Well now, little Miss Iceberg!' He grinned fatly and offensively. Katy glanced quickly at Laurence, but he met her eyes with a cold and dispassionate stare. Hunt put a heavy arm round her shoulders.

'Now isn't this just a lovely surprise?' He gestured expansively. 'I've always said, Larry, that you run into everybody at Cannes. There we all were having a nice little dinner, with Freddie and—Jane, is it? And we'd *just* made the interesting discovery that we have, shall I say, mutual friends . . . and I look up, and what do I see? My hot-tempered little researcher, who turns out to be pretty hot in other respects as well . . .'

Katy knew her face was white with anger and shock; she

could feel Laurence Martineau's lazy gaze. Camilla Drew's
eyes were fixed on Katy's shoulder, where the marks of his
fingers were only too visible. She had never felt so tawdry or
so cheap in her life.

'Sit down, honey.' Dick Hunt was gawping unapologetically
at the neckline of her dress. 'We've finished our meal, but we
can all have some brandy, can't we? What do you say, Larry?'

The actor's stony gaze met hers across the table. Katy hesitated. She couldn't wait to get out, but her nerve was coming
back. Laurence wasn't going to give her any help, she could
see that, perhaps it would be better to brazen it out?

She took the brandy glass Dick Hunt was already holding
out to her, and attempted a smile.

'Why not?' she said lightly. 'It might be fun.'

But before she could sit down, Freddie and Jane arrived at
the table, and there was a flurry of introductions. In the midst
of them, Laurence suddenly rose. He made an odd stiff half-
bow to Camilla Drew, who had been sitting there all the while
looking totally composed, a little smile playing around her
beautiful mouth

'I'm sorry,' he said curtly. 'Katharine and I were just leaving.'

'No, we weren't,' Katy said rebelliously. 'I wanted to speak
to Jane . . .'

Dick Hunt patted her hand. 'That's my girl,' he said, grinning across the table at Laurence Martineau. 'The night is
young, I say. What's the hurry, Larry? We're interrupting your
little tête-à-tête, is that it?'

For a moment, Katy thought with sick horror that the scene
at Angelo's was to be re-enacted there and then. She saw
Laurence's fist curl; the tension around the table was electric,
and Freddie and Jane, sensing it, watched wide-eyed.

The two men glared across the table at each other; a battle
of wills was going on, and Katy knew that she was somehow a
pawn. It was Camilla Drew who resolved it.

'Do sit down, Dick,' she said in her soft whispery voice. She
gave a little yawn, like a cat, and fixed Katy with the sweetest
of smiles. 'I'm terribly tired,' she went on gently. 'We mustn't
keep Laurence and Katy, must we, Laurence? If Katy wants
to see her friend, why don't you invite them back to La
Bayardière for a drink? You ought to see the house, Freddie—

Jane. It's quite lovely . . .'

'There was a moment's silence. Dick Hunt sat down abruptly. Katy suddenly had the oddest sensation that it was this quiet woman who possessed the most formidable will amongst them. She spoke almost hesitantly, and yet it was instantly obvious that she would get her way. Laurence Martineau looked from her to Katy, and hesitated only a moment.

'What a good idea,' he said in an odd manner. 'That solves everything, doesn't it, Camilla? Shall we go?'

He pushed past the table, and Katy felt him grasp her elbow like an iron vice.

'You have a car, Freddie? Good, then if you come now you can follow us—it's difficult to give directions . . .'

Before Katy could even say goodnight, he was propelling her across the dining room, Freddie and Jane meekly in tow. In seconds they had crossed the gauntlet of stares, swept past the maître d'hôtel, and were out on the terrace. The sudden cold of the night air hit Katy like a jet of cold water; suddenly she realised how much wine she had drunk earlier, and she almost stumbled. Laurence held her up, and half dragged her across the road to his car. He shouted a few instructions to Freddie, and opened the car door.

'Get in,' he said, and there was no politeness in his voice, just a cold fury.

Katy shivered, suddenly afraid, as he pushed her roughly inside the Lagonda. The effects of the wine still hadn't worn off, and the rapid succession of events had left her feeling slightly hysterical. It occurred to her that he had spoken to her like that once before, the night they had left Angelo's. They had been together in a restaurant only three times, she thought suddenly, and each time it had ended in trouble. She felt close to tears, but she didn't cry. Instead she laughed, an odd choked sound that she hardly recognised. Laurence heard it. He leant across the seat and gripped her hand so tightly that it hurt.

'If you do that again, I shall slap your face,' he muttered. 'If you know what's good for you, you'll keep your mouth shut until we get back to the house. It was you who felt she had to talk to her friend, remember?'

He slammed the car into gear, wrenched the wheel, jammed

his foot down on the accelerator, and the powerful engine
soared into life. They screeched along the Croisette, and up on
to the autoroute. Katy could see the speedometer rising: eighty
miles an hour, ninety, a hundred. He's going to kill us, she
thought, but he didn't, he just swung the car expertly off on to
the narrow country roads, the pace hardly slackening.

A high wind was buffeting the car—the mistral at last. Katy
thought dully—and it was bitterly cold. But the cold did her
some good, for gradually she felt her mind beginning to clear.
As the effects of the wine began to wear off, the full awfulness
of everything that had happened bore in on her. And now the
ghastly comedy would have to continue, she thought, with
Freddie and Jane as witnesses. She hoped fervently that they
might have lost the others—it seemed quite likely at the pace
they were driving. What had happened already was bad
enough; she couldn't bear to prolong it.

But it was not just the cheapness of her own behaviour, or
the memory of the contemptuous way Laurence had handled
her, that made her cheeks burn with shame in the darkness of
the car. Another realisation had come to her, a suspicion that
grew and grew as they drove. *That* was why he had made those
trips to Cannes, suddenly she was sure of it. *That* was why he
had been so reluctant to talk about it. It wasn't a mistress he
had been visiting—it was his beautiful ex-wife, the woman who
caused him so much pain he never spoke of her.

Was he attempting a reconciliation? she wondered. Maybe
they were reconciled already—after all, there was no reason
why an ex-wife shouldn't also be a mistress . . . And suddenly,
as the thought came to her, she knew why Camilla Drew
seemed familiar. It wasn't her face, it was her *voice*. It was *she*
who had telephoned the previous morning. In despair she
rested her aching head against the cool glass of the window as
the car lurched around the hairpin bends. She didn't understand any of it, she thought. She felt caught up in a horrible
web of intrigue and duplicity, and she was certain of only one
thing in the whole ugly mess, and that was Laurence's attitude
to her. If he had had any respect for her before, she had destroyed it that night, efficiently and completely.

She looked at the cold, hard profile of the man beside her,
his eyes intent on the road, his mouth set in a hard line. She
had been right earlier that evening, she thought suddenly,

before they had even left the house. He just wanted to go to bed with her. His hesitation had been minimal, and now it was gone. At the first sign of encouragement, he'd been happy to take what he could, and humiliate her into the bargain. She hated him in that moment, and was filled with a bitter anger and jealousy. What did he want her for anyway? Couldn't Camilla Drew give him whatever it was he was looking for?

They had reached La Bayardière. The courtyard was in darkness as the car screeched to a halt.

'Get out,' he said curtly.

Katy fumbled with the catch on the door, and heard him curse with impatience. He leaned across and opened it, and as he did so a blast of wind hit the car, almost knocking her off her feet.

'Hurry up,' he ordered. 'Get inside.'

As Katy ran for the steps, the first rain suddenly began, lashing down on her bare head and shoulders. She raced for the house, hearing his footsteps behind her. Inside the hall, she hesitated. Perhaps they had managed to lose Freddie and Jane ... perhaps she just had time to get to her room. The hall door smashed back in a gust of wind and rain, and Laurence ducked in, his jacket soaked, his hair running with water.

'Where are you going?' He glared at her from the doorway. 'Don't bother to answer—I'll tell you.' He came across and gripped her wrist. 'You're staying right here. You can play the charming hostess for once. Your friends have just driven in, and I'd advise you to look after them.'

'Or?' She tried to shake off his hand, feeling suddenly angry. Whatever she had done, he had no right to threaten her.

'Or there'll be trouble.' He gave her a cold smile. 'It's as simple as that. As you once said, I have a talent for making scenes—especially with an audience. Go and make some coffee—I'll go and fetch them.'

He ducked out into the rain again, leaving Katy rubbing her painful wrist. Hastily she made for the kitchen. She didn't dare go upstairs—he'd only follow her if she did. Perhaps if she did what he said the whole ghastly charade might pass off somehow ...

She could hear voices and laughter outside in the hall as, with trembling hands, she put the kettle to boil, found cups, found the coffee. Someone laughed, and there were stampings as if people were trying to get the wet off their clothes and shoes.

'Come into the study,' she heard Laurence say. 'There's a fire lit—you can dry out. Freddie, Jane—what can I get you? Katharine is just making some coffee, but there's brandy, or whisky . . .'

She heard no more; the door must have shut. In despair, she sat down at the kitchen table and rested her head in her hands. She felt exhausted. She couldn't take much more of this. If only she could get away from it all, go back to England . . .

She heard a soft tap on the door, and, as she looked up, fighting back tears of strain and tiredness, Jane came in. She made a gesture as if she were fanning herself, and grinned.

'Wow!' she exclaimed. 'What the hell is going on, Katy? I thought we were going to be pulling you out of a ditch the way he drove back here, and the atmosphere at that table— phew! You could have cut it with a knife!'

Katy shrugged. 'It's a long story,' she said tiredly. 'And if I start telling you he'll only come in and interrupt us. Let's skip it, shall we?'

Jane came across to her quickly, and put an arm around her shoulders.

'Hey, love,' she said gently, 'you look all in. Are you O.K.?'

Katy nodded. 'I'm fine. I had too much to drink earlier— that's all. It's wearing off now.'

Jane looked at her keenly. 'Well, you can tell me one thing anyway,' she said. 'You're having an affair with him, aren't you?'

Katy looked away. 'I don't suppose you'll believe me,' she said slowly, 'but actually, no, I'm not.'

Jane sat down at the table and lit a cigarette. She watched Katy closely while she made the coffee.

'Well,' she said finally, 'I'm sure advice is the last thing you need at the moment. But I'm sure of one thing. There's something funny going on—I can't make it out at all. It was pure chance that Freddie and I met Dick Hunt. But I'm *not* sure it was chance that we all ran into you tonight.'

'What do you mean?'

'I'll tell you. It was Hunt's idea to go to the Carlton, right? We turn up, and it strikes me straight away there's a funny atmosphere. We're introduced to Camilla whatsit, I haven't a clue who she is—I'm awful with names, remember? But it's as if there's some private joke going on between her and Hunt Halfway through the meal—I haven't spotted you yet—*she* says to him, "Well, look, Dick, isn't that Larry over there with that pretty young girl?" Whereupon he goes through a great act, gasps, surprise, etc.—and recognises you. Except he's not a very good actor. I had the distinct impression they both knew about you all along, *and* they weren't surprised to see you there. That's all. And I'll tell you one other thing for nothing. I don't like her much. Too much sweetness and light by half. I thought the whole thing was pretty weird, I didn't even realise she was the ex-Mrs Martineau until Freddie told me, and then I began to twig. If you ask me, she was rabidly jealous——'

'That's possible,' Katy interrupted her. 'I think—well, I think they've been seeing each other again . . .'

Jane's eyebrows rose. 'You don't say? The plot thickens. And where do you stand in all this, love?'

'Nowhere,' said Katy bitterly. 'I'd better just get the coffee, that's all.'

Jane rose and helped her with the tray. By the door she paused.

'One last thing,' she said gently, 'before we go back and face your terrifying actor friend. Are you happy here, Katy? Because if not, just say the word. Freddie and I are going back tomorrow, we could easily book another seat—you can come with us if it's all got a bit much.'

Katy pressed her hand.

'You're very kind,' she said. 'I'll think about it—all right? Let's just leave it for now—if you give me the name of your hotel, I'll ring you in the morning.'

Jane grinned. 'O.K.,' she said cheerily. 'It's your funeral! We're at the Metropole, and the flight's at three. Freddie and I are available for emergency escort if needed. Don't forget.'

They went back into the study, to find Laurence and Freddie sitting by the fire. Both were drinking brandy, and Freddie looked ill at ease. It wasn't difficult to see why, Katy thought miserably. Laurence was perfectly charming—he helped with the tray, drew chairs up for both of them, fetched brandy for

Katy—none of which erased the black anger that blazed in his eyes.

The conversation was sporadic and awkward, with long silences, followed by moments when Freddie or Jane both spoke nervously at once. Having exhausted the topics of the mistral, La Bayardière itself, and the food at the Carlton, there seemed nothing left to say. Freddie was chain-smoking, and kept looking nervously at his watch; Jane continued to make valiant efforts to keep the conversation going; Katy said practically nothing.

'Well, why don't you ask about all your friends in London, Katharine?' Laurence's voice cut coldly through another of the pauses. 'I'm sure you're anxious to hear how they all are . . .'

Katy didn't answer, and Jane cut in.

'Oh, everybody's fine,' she said quickly. 'Though it's not the same without you, Katy love. We all miss you, you know. Do you know yet when you're coming back?'

She glanced at Laurence as she said this, and Katy knew the remark was for his benefit.

'I . . . I haven't quite decided yet,' she said quietly. 'That is, I don't yet know when . . .'

'Well, don't leave it too long, love,' Jane said airily. 'You can't miss the great wedding, you know. It's at the end of next month. Mandy's living on cottage cheese until then and she's bought a size twelve wedding dress already as incentive . . .'

'Ah yes, the wedding.' Laurence looked across at Katy, his eyes glittering dangerously. 'It was all rather sudden, wasn't it?'

'I'll say!' Jane laughed. 'I'd always thought he was madly in love with Katy here—everyone thought so. Maybe he still is. I shouldn't be surprised. The whole thing's a mystery to me.'

'Well, I'm sure Katy won't want to miss it anyway, will you, Katy?' He gave a charming smile which failed to erase the anger in his eyes. 'I'm sure she'll be there, she's such a romantic—as you all saw tonight.'

There was another ghastly silence, during which Laurence Martineau looked pointedly at his watch. Freddie was instantly on his feet, one cue being enough. Katy felt her cheeks burn with embarrassment and shame, and she knew everyone in the room noticed it.

Jane stood up, and glared at Laurence.

'Well, if Katy's a romantic,' she said stoutly, 'she's none the worse for that.' She came across, and gave her friend a warm hug. 'Don't be too long getting back, love,' she said. 'The flat's not the same without you. I'll maybe talk to you in the morning, before the flight—right?' She gave Katy a meaningful nod, and ran her hands through her mop of platinum curls.

'Right, Freddie,' she said, 'we'll be off, then. Thanks for the drink, Mr Martineau, and sorry to have barged in like that. Look after Katy for us, won't you?'

Freddie also mumbled his thanks, and Katy felt a momentary wave of sympathy for him, he looked so hangdog and miserable, and then the two of them made for the door. With elaborate and icy courtesy, Laurence insisted on showing them down to their car. Katy waved from the doorway, then quickly ducked in again out of the rain. She just had time to get her bag from the study, she thought, and then, with luck, she might escape upstairs before he had a chance to get back. She found the bag, and had got as far as the stairs when the front door was flung back.

'I think not,' Laurence said curtly.

'Please,' Katy said, 'I want to go to bed . . .'

'That comes later,' he said viciously. 'Just at the moment I want to talk to you. The comedy isn't over yet, and it was you—if you recall—who was so keen to prolong it.'

Before she could say a word he had propelled her back into the study. Then he slammed the door and locked it.

'Now.' He put the key in his pocket. 'We'll continue the scenario, I think. Maybe you'd better start by explaining just what in hell you think you've been up to . . .'

Instinctively Katy backed away from him. He was savagely, furiously angry, and now he was making no attempt to hide it. She had never seen a man look at a woman like that before, and for a moment she thought he was going to hit her. He took a step towards her, and her hand came up automatically to shield her face. His eyes glinted as he registered her reaction. He stopped, about three feet away from her, and Katy realised she was cornered. Behind her was the fireplace; to the side his desk . . . Suddenly those reports from the divorce courts she had read all those weeks before flooded back into her memory: *mental cruelty and tales of physical violence.* Was this what had driven Camilla Drew away from him? She hardly recognised in this man the gentle, considerate host of the past month. It was like the time he had been drunk . . . but this time he wasn't drunk, she knew that. He was totally in control. His glass of brandy, untouched, stood on the table.

'Now.' His voice was flat, devoid of emotion. 'Before we begin, you can take that dress off.'

'What?' Katy felt herself go cold with fear.

'You heard me. Take that dress off.'

Katy said nothing, and she did not move. She felt paralysed with terror, and her mind seemed frozen. She thought of crying out for help, but she knew it was useless. There was no one else in the house, and outside the wind was whining ceaselessly.

'Take it off.'

'I shall do no such thing,' she said, suddenly finding her voice, and surprised at the strength of it.

'Then I shall.'

He took a step towards her, and Katy shrank back. She raised her hands in front of her.

'Don't you dare!' she snapped, her voice high and uncontrolled. 'If you touch me, I'll . . .'

He took no notice. His insolent angry eyes never left her face. Very slowly and deliberately he reached up a hand to one of the thin diamanté straps. It all seemed to be happening to Katy very slowly, at a dream pace, or in that state of slowed and intensified consciousness that can happen in a road accident. As his hand brushed her skin, she caught her breath sharply; then, suddenly, instinct took over. Hardly knowing what she was doing, she twisted, drew back her hand and hit him across the face with her full strength. As she did so there was a ripping sound, and the thin chiffon tore, Laurence stepped back, and Katy felt the silk slip from her shoulders, down over her breasts to her waist. They both stood there in sudden silence, and Katy drew in a long, shuddering breath. She let the material hang as it had fallen. Suddenly she didn't care any more; she was beyond all modesty, and the tears that came to her eyes were tears of anger.

'Very well,' she said finally, her voice tight and strained. 'Are you satisfied now?'

'No,' he said shortly.

He was standing back, his arms folded, an angry red weal down the side of his face where she had hit him. She felt his eyes rake her coldly from head to foot—her hair tumbled over her shoulders, her pale breasts untanned, above the black folds of her dress that now spilled on the floor in a pool of dark silk. Her breasts rose, as she fought to control her breath— she felt as if she were choking.

'Please,' she said, despising herself for the pleading note she could hear in her voice, 'may I go now?'

'No, you may not,' he said. 'I haven't finished.'

He lifted his hand, and Katy flinched, then forced herself to stand still. She wouldn't move, she thought, she wouldn't speak, she would shame him into stopping all this ... Very deliberately he reached across and ran one finger down her face, very softly, over her cheekbones to her lips, then down the curve of her neck to the hollow at the base of her throat, then down farther ... Involuntarily, she closed her eyes; her body trembled under his touch, and his hand tightened over her breast. Then she opened her eyes, and saw that his expression had changed.

All anger had left it; he looked exhausted, and the pain was back in those dark eyes.

'So very lovely,' he said finally, and he removed his hand.

Even then, even under those circumstances, her whole body cried out for him to replace it, and she fought not to let him see it. There was a silence, during which they both looked at each other, and it lengthened unbearably. Then he shrugged, and half turned away.

'All right, Katharine,' he said, and his voice sounded drained of all feeling. 'Just tell me—which are you? The woman in this study this morning, or the woman I took out tonight? Just tell me that, and then by all means, go.'

She was trembling all over; now they had reached the real moment of reckoning, and she knew it. Words jumbled themselves in her mind, a desire to tell the truth fought with a desire to protect what she felt from his knowledge.

'Which do you want?' she countered finally, and she had to force the words out because her lips felt stiff and numb. It wasn't the right reply, and she knew it before he answered her.

'What makes you think I want either of them?' he said coldly.

CHAPTER NINE

KATY felt as if he had hit her across the face, and her skin drained of all colour. She bent forward and pulled up the material of her dress, holding it awkwardly and hoping that the veil of her hair hid the expression on her face. There was another silence, and she knew in a minute she would break down. She tried to breathe slowly to calm herself, and to her own surprise, it worked. Suddenly the confusion in her mind quieted, the tension in her subsided. What he had said to her this morning, in this room, suddenly came back to her with total clarity: she could hear his voice saying the words as if he spoke them at that moment, and she suddenly felt at peace. What did it matter now? She had nothing left to lose.

'This morning, you said . . .' she hesitated. 'You said that if one cared for someone——' she risked looking at him, and nearly stopped, but he stood quite still and made no attempt to prompt or interrupt her. 'If one . . . loved someone, then one shouldn't hide it. One should be proud of it. You said.'

He sighed, and she went on, gaining confidence.

'Well, I think you were right to say that. It was honest and—anyway, I told you then what I felt. I . . . I meant what I said them. I meant it with my whole heart. I do . . . love you.'

She saw his head turn sharply away, and she rushed on, because she knew she had to finish before he interrupted her.

'It's all right,' she said, 'I know what you feel. I know you don't love me, and it was . . . perfectly honest of you not to pretend. I mean, another man might have done, if he had wanted . . .'

'Wanted what, Katharine?'

She felt the colour rush up to her neck and into her cheeks.

'Well, wanted to . . . go to bed with me. But you didn't pretend, and I suppose you didn't want to hurt me, and I was grateful for that. But tonight, I thought, I don't care. I wanted you to want me . . . to desire me, because that was enough, don't you understand? I wanted you to treat me like a woman, to see that I was a woman, not just a silly girl, and I had this dress and I'd never worn it before, so I thought I would try to ... to be beguiling, and sophisticated, and seductive ...'

'You thought you would *try* to be seductive?' he said drily. She saw a ghost of a smile begin on his lips, and, afraid he was about to mock her, she rushed on.

'I know I was no good at it, and I hated myself, I didn't believe all those things I said. But you ... you responded, and I thought that *was* what you wanted me to be. Then I could see how contemptuous you were, and I hated you and I hated myself. And then——' she drew a deep breath. 'Then I saw your wife ...'

'My ex-wife.'

'Yes, well, Camilla Drew, and I realised why you'd been going to Cannes all those afternoons, and why you would never talk about her, and why you always looked in such pain when—marriage—was mentioned, because I suppose you love her still, and she's—well, she's so beautiful.'

She finished in a rush, all the words tumbling over one another, and there was a long silence. The blood was pounding in her head, and all she could think was that if he didn't speak, didn't say something soon, she would go mad. But he didn't. He just stood there quietly looking at her, his eyes shadowed. In the end, it was Katy who broke the long silence.

'So,' she said, her voice sounding high and forced, 'to answer your original question. I *was* acting tonight. But you see ... in a sense I've been acting ever since I came here. I didn't want you to know what I felt. What I've felt ever since I first met you ...'

'I see.'

He moved towards her again, so they were very close, and tilted her face up to him so that she had to meet his eyes. They were suddenly gentle.

'You've forgotten something,' he said gravely.

She stared up at him, wordlessly.

'You've forgotten what I said to you this morning, in here. I wasn't lying, Kate. I never lie.' He smiled, and corrected himself. 'Well, very rarely. I have told you one lie.'

She felt the pain starting up again. She didn't want to know what it was, she thought miserably.

'Listen to me, Kate,' he said urgently. He put his arms around her, and drew her towards him. There was a ghost of mockery in his eyes, and he smiled.

'I—er—lied about my secretary.'

'*What?*' she drew back, startled, her mind instantly racing. His *secretary*? Could it be that . . .?

'I told you she was getting married. That was the lie.'

'I see,' she said dully.

'No,' he said, 'I don't think you do, Kate. My secretary . . .' he paused teasingly. 'My secretary is fifty-five, and a dear woman, but she hasn't married, and isn't likely to. I wouldn't say, on the whole, that marriage is on *her* horizon.'

'But I don't understand,' Katy stammered. 'Then why . . .?'

'I gave her an unexpected holiday,' he said drily. 'I thought it was a rather good idea at the time. I was in a certain flat in London, in Little Venice, as it happened, and suddenly I thought, how can I contrive to see this wilful and idealistic young woman again? I know, I'll offer her a job.' He smiled ruefully. 'Not very original, I'm afraid, but it was the best I could do at the time. And so I rang my real secretary and arranged for her to have a little break . . .'

Katy stared at him in bewilderment, and somewhere within her, though she fought to suppress it, she felt a ghostly hope begin to rise.

'Why did you do that?' she asked steadily.

'Dear Kate.' He pressed her closer to him. 'You can be very blind, you know. I did tell you, this morning. That's what you've forgotten. I wanted you, Kate, wanted you desperately. I had to see you again. I had to have you near me . . . and so——' he broke off. 'My secretary was delighted. Her brother has a little flat in Cannes—she's there now. She's been there all the time you've been at La Bayardière. So I had an escape clause, you see—if you turned out to type at ten words a minute, and not to be a very . . . good secretary.'

'In Cannes?' Suddenly Katy felt her heart lift. 'All this while! So that was why you went there! It wasn't to see Camilla, it was to see her!'

The words were hardly out before she saw his face change. A shadow passed over it, and with a sickening lurch of her heart she knew she was wrong.

'No,' he said quietly, 'you were right the first time, Kate. I went to Cannes to see Camilla.'

He saw the hope and happiness drain from her face, and pulled her fiercely towards him.

'Kate, you must listen to me, you must believe me. There were—there are—reasons why I had to see Camilla. I can't explain them now; it's all too long and too ugly. What I said tonight was true. Our marriage was a living hell. I paid for it then, and I've been paying for the last five years, ever since that farce of a divorce ... Kate, you must believe me.'

She stared at him wordlessly, thinking of all those long absences, and thinking of the woman she had seen that night. That sweet, pale face, with the long hair falling over her shoulders ...

'I don't know,' she said haltingly, 'I don't know. She's so ...'

'I'll tell you what she is,' he said savagely. 'One day I'll tell you. Soon, I promise you, Kate. But not now. Look at me, Kate, for God's sake. It's written all over my face, isn't it? I want you, Kate. I ... I have wanted you, all the time you've been here. It's been driving me insane, having you so close, not being able to touch you, thinking all the time you belonged to some other man. Why do you think I got drunk that day after the beach? Because I knew if I didn't I wouldn't be able to keep my hands off you. And tonight—that dress. I was so angry I hardly knew what I was doing. But I had to find out—which woman you were: the one I wanted, or the one you were acting. And also—I'm a man, Kate, for God's sake—and I've been living like a monk all these weeks. I wanted you tonight, Kate. I wanted to see you—like this.'

His hands moved down, touching hers where they still held the torn folds of her dress before her. He pulled them away, so the silk slipped down against her skin once more, and her breasts were bared to his caress.

'Kate.' She could hear the desire he felt roughening his voice, feel it hardening his strong body, and her own desire answered it, silencing the last few doubts in her mind. With a low moan she pressed herself to him. His mouth sought hers with a blind urgency; his kiss was without gentleness or restraint. It hurt her and it pleasured her, as his hands did exploring her body. She was caught up in a vortex of pain and pleasure that mixed and married and sucked her under until her mind was gone. There were no thoughts left, just the urgency of touching, feeling, reaching. She felt captive, but also exultant in a wild new freedom, and she knew at last that she could touch him, with all the pent-up longing of those last weeks. He took her hands and guided them, teaching her blind fingertips the new language of a man's body, over, along, down, to the hard demanding core of his being. She felt him shudder under her touch, as she trembled under his, and the violent power of feelings she had never known became a maddening compulsion. She wanted there to be no barriers between them, and her hands fumbled at the clothes that hindered the release of skin against skin. She wanted him on her and in her, filling her with that hard male strength, and she knew he wanted the same, for his hands pulled at the silk of her dress, which was ripping with his impatience.

He swore. Then his hands stilled, grasped hers, and stilled them. He held her tight against him, and the room seemed filled with the pulse of their hearts, with their rough breathing.

'Laurence,' she pleaded, struggling to free her hands, to touch him again.

'No. Darling Kate, no.' His mouth was against her throat.

'I want . . .'

'I know what you want. Dear God, do you think I don't want it too?'

'Then . . .'

'No,' he said fiercely. 'I will have you—I must have you. But not yet. And don't touch me again, Kate. I've hardly any will left, and if you do, you'll break it. Now,' he held her hands fiercely, so she could not move, and gradually she calmed. 'Now,' he said, 'I want you to listen to me.'

'Very well.' She said it demurely, but she knew her eyes were dancing with happiness.

'Little witch!' He kissed her forehead lightly. 'Listen to me.'

His face was serious once more, and she waited silently.

'Kate——' he hesitated, 'I . . . I want you to stay here.'

'Then I'll stay,' she said simply.

He shook his head. 'No,' he said gravely, 'not like that. It's impossible. My secretary can't stay on holiday indefinitely. Besides . . .' his eyes dropped, 'I saw tonight what I'm keeping you from—London, your friends, proper work . . . I have no right to do that.'

'I don't want to go back to London,' she cried impulsively. 'Please believe me. I don't want to at all. If I can't stay here as your secretary, then I'll be . . .'

She broke off, and the colour flooded into her face. He

looked at her mockingly.

'My mistress, Kate? Is that what you were going to suggest? I believe it was.'

'If you wanted.' She turned her face away.

'I don't think that would do.' He paused, hesitating. 'Of course,' he went on slowly, 'if you wanted, there are other ways. It would be a pity to cause a scandal in the village, don't you think? You could stay here, Kate . . . as my wife.'

She jerked her face upwards to see if he were mocking her, her eyes widening.

'As your *wife*?'

He smiled. 'Don't look so shocked. I am a free man. Not in the eyes of my church, of course. But legally . . .' He broke off, and his eyes darkened. 'Would you marry me, Kate?'

She stared at him wordlessly, her mind suddenly in tumult. Her lips opened to frame an answer, but before she could speak he raised his hand, and placed it gently on her lips.

'No,' he said softly, 'don't answer now. You mustn't. Not after all this, and not until I've explained everything to you. I have no right to ask you, not yet. Think, Kate. You can tell me . . . tomorrow.'

And before she could say a word, he gathered her into his arms, lifting her easily, as if she were weightless. He unlocked the door and carried her upstairs to his room.

Gently he laid her down on the bed, and she reached her arms up to him, aching with longing.

'No,' he said, with mock sternness, 'don't tempt me. Not yet. I want you to sleep. I'll stay with you.'

He drew the covers over her like a child, then he left her. Katy could just see him, in the dim light, standing by the shutters, staring out through the slats to the moonlight and the wail of the mistral. Her head sank back on the cool pillows. She would do as Laurence said, she thought, as exhaustion swept over her. Then, in the morning, she would answer his last question, and . . . She listened to the rhythmic gusts of wind, listened for the sound of his breathing. He would wake her in the morning, she thought joyfully. On the sound of the mistral, she difted suddenly into sleep.

She woke late, and she saw at once that Laurence was gone. In a second, she passed from the peace of sleep to the agitation

of waking. Where was he? She listened for sounds in the
house—perhaps he was in the kitchen—but everything was
totally silent. All she could hear, muted by the glass and the
shutters, was the continuing whine of the mistral. Instantly
she pushed back the covers, and in bare feet, holding her torn
dress around her, she raced along the corridor and down the
stairs. The study, the drawing room, the kitchen—they were
all empty; the morning's letters still lay on the stone floor in
the hall. Shivering with cold, Katy raced upstairs again, feeling
suddenly frightened. Wildly she opened doors to rooms they
never used. They were all silent, shuttered, the furniture
swathed in white sheets. Her own room; it was empty, just as
she had left it the night before. She went back down the corridor to Laurence's room, seeing it for the first time clearly.
How bare it was! White walls, a few rugs and books; no
pictures. A sudden crash from outside made her freeze, motionless. She flung back the shutters. A chair, blown over by the
wind, careered along the stones of the terrace, jammed by a
wall and lay still. She turned back into the room, her heart
beating wildly, suddenly possessed with a cold premonition.
Something was wrong. Where was he?

Then she saw the note. It was lying on the end of the bed,
half hidden, where she had pushed back the sheets. Feverishly
she unfolded it, and stared at the paper. All it said was: *I have
to go into Cannes. I must see Camilla. Trust me.* There was no
signature. She read and re-read the few words, trying to calm
herself. But *why* had he gone, why *then*, after all that had
happened? He had said he would stay . . .

She forced herself to be calm. She went back to her bedroom, bathed, and dressed, hardly conscious of what she was
doing. She took the note and folded it—in half, in quarters, in
eighths—and held it against her skin like a talisman. She
looked at her watch. It was nearly eleven; if Laurence had left
before the morning letters came, he must have left very early.
Perhaps he would be back soon. Yes, surely he would. At any
moment she might hear his footsteps on the terrace.

She went downstairs to the kitchen, grateful for the warmth
from the range, for it was bitterly cold. It was Monday, she
realised; market day; Marie-Christine would have gone to
Toulon. She made herself some coffee, and sat sipping it by
the stove. All that had happened the night before flooded back

into her mind. Compulsively she tried to recall exactly, step by step, what had occurred, what had been said But her memories were fractured, her mind leapt from one thing to another. Laurence had asked her to marry him, she thought, and for the first time that morning she recaptured the amazing happiness she had felt as she had fallen asleep in his room. But before *that*. He had said—what?

He had told her about his secretary, that was it. He had told her how much he wanted her, and . . . Suddenly she felt a chill fear again. He had not said he loved her. No. he hadn't. and he never told lies . . .

She felt pain and panic well up in her. Last night she had had no doubts, but now, in the chill empty house, they flooded in on her. He *didn't* love her, then. He'd talked of marriage and avoiding scandal in the same breath; he wouldn't sleep with her. Could he offer to marry her just for the sake of convention, she thought, because it was against his moral code to take a girl as a mistress? Yes, she thought, he might, and she remembered his odd fierce rectitude, how he had wanted her, he had said, all those weeks and never touched her—yes, he might. Or perhaps—perhaps there was some other reason, something she didn't know, something to do with Camilla. Oh, why had he left her that morning? she cried desperately to herself. Why, why?

For the hundredth time she took out his note and read it again. *Trust me*. She must, she thought. She must just wait. So she forced herself to tidy the kitchen, to wash the glasses and cups from the night before. She went into the study and busied herself lighting a fire. For his return, she told herself.

At twelve, suddenly, she heard a car. Her heart lifted, and she listened intently, but the wind was howling outside, and she couldn't be certain if it had turned into the house. Then she heard footsteps. He was back! Joyfully, she rushed out into the hall. She fumbled with the locks in her haste, and as she threw it back, the blast of the wind hit her. Dick Hunt was standing in the doorway, one hand just raised to the bell-pull.

Involuntarily she backed away, and he smiled widely.

'Katy, my sweet. Can we come in? We're frozen.'

Before the 'we' had time to register they were inside, Dick Hunt pulling a ridiculous fur coat tighter round him and shivering, and Camilla Drew, right behind him.

'Shut the door, Katy love,' he said. 'There's a bloody gale blowing, or haven't you noticed?'

Automatically she shut the door, and as the sound of the wind was cut off there was silence. She stood with her back to the door, and looked at them.

Dick Hunt was stamping his feet, as if to get back the circulation. Camilla Drew had sailed straight past Katy and was now standing in the middle of the hall. Even in this cold, hard light, she looked lovely, and totally at ease. Katy's first thought, bizarrely, was that the mistress of the house had returned. She felt as if she were a servant, as if she ought to take her coat, rush to make her comfortable.

Camilla was wearing a coat which looked like sable; certainly it wasn't mink, and it was exquisite. It was dark, and full, cut like a military trenchcoat; it fell to just below the knees. Below that were beautiful boots, like riding boots, highly polished. Her pale hair was tied back with a dark ribbon, and she looked about twenty years old. As Katy stared, bitterly aware of the shabby jeans and stretched sweater she herself was wearing, Camilla raised a long slender hand and brushed a strand of hair away from her beautiful pale face. She looked indescribably fragile and delicate, and yet she possessed and commanded the room. Katy felt herself shrinking from her presence. Camilla said nothing, and once again Katy had the sensation she had had in Cannes the night before, of being dominated, taken over. She felt rooted to the spot, and she stared at the other woman in total admiration.

Finally she found her voice.

'I'm afraid Laurence isn't here,' she said, trying to make her voice level and normal. 'He's gone to Cannes.'

'I know,' said Camilla Drew, in that soft whispery voice. 'He's gone to see me, I'm afraid, and I've sent him on a terrible goose-chase.'

'We haven't come to see Laurence, Katy love.' Dick Hunt gave her one of the horrible greasy smiles she remembered so well. 'We've come to see you.'

'To see me?' Katy said stiffly. 'But why? I don't understand. Why should you . . .'

Camilla Drew was unbuttoning her coat, and Dick Hunt hurried to help her out of it. With perfect composure (this had been her house, Katy thought, and felt sick), she hung it up on the pegs over Laurence's old jacket. Dick Hunt hung up his. They glanced at each other, as if to decide on a cue, and Camilla turned.

'It's my fault, Katharine,' she said. 'If you want us to go, then please say so, and of course we will, but you see, after last night I felt I had to talk to you.'

Her voice was so low that Katy could hardly catch what she said, and she made no attempt to raise it. If you're ready to leave, why hang up your coats as if you owned the place? Katy thought angrily, but she didn't say anything; somehow she felt it would be unpardonably gross to be rude to her.

Camilla looked at her for a moment, and then, to her total astonishment, she crossed the hall and very gently took Katy's hands in hers.

'Katharine,' she said, in that soft, pulsing voice, 'I feel as if I know you already. I've heard so much about you. Please, I think I understand a little of what you must feel, but I do so want to talk to you. Would you let me?'

Her touch was soft, her hands cool, and she looked up at Katy with the same expression she had had the night before. It was one of total sympathy, a woman speaking directly to another woman, knowing her feelings and respecting them, and it produced a most curious effect. Katy could feel her will being sapped. Her mind resisted, but weakly.

Dick Hunt was suddenly at her elbow. 'Sweetie,' he said urgently, 'I know what you think of me, and I know we haven't had a chance to talk since—well, since all that mess in London—and I know what kind of a girl you are, headstrong and so on. In fact, I told Camilla we'd be wasting our time, but she insisted on coming, didn't you, Camilla?'

Katy expected her to assent, but she ignored him, and he bumbled on.

'I know you think the worst of me, Katy. But there's a lot you don't know, and—well, the truth is, I want you back on the programme, though that's not the most important thing. You were the best researcher I've had, do you know that? I know I fired you, and I was pretty rough that day, but I've always had a vile temper, and to tell you the truth, I was feeling pretty sore that morning, and not just physically either!'

Katy looked at him with a cold dislike, turning her eyes from Camilla Drew's face with difficulty. That's it, she thought, wriggle. You're pulling something and I don't believe a word you say, Dick Hunt. I've worked with you! I know you and your vile tempers.

'Dick,' Camilla Drew turned to him. 'Do you think you could find us some coffee? The kitchen's through there—I'm sure you'll manage. I really do want to talk to Katharine, and we haven't got long.'

It was the sweetest, the softest of dismissals as she said it. Dick Hunt took it like a spaniel dog; without another word, he turned in the direction of the kitchen.

Before his back was turned Camilla turned to Katy again, and with some part of her brain that struggled to remain an observer to all this, Katy noted that her eyes were not blue as they appeared in photographs but a curious deep violet. She took Katy's arm and led her gently into the study. Then she sat down opposite her, fixing those violet eyes on Katy's face. Stiffly Katy too sat down. She looked at Camilla covertly. She was not as she had expected, Katy thought. She didn't look hard or chic; she wore a simple grey dress a little too large for her, which emphasised her frail vulnerability. Her beautiful pale face was etched with the finest of lines around the eyes and mouth, but they looked like the marks of strain, not age.

'How old are you, Katharine?' she asked suddenly, taking Katy off her guard.

'Twenty-three.'

Camilla sighed. 'Twenty-three! Do you know how old I was when I met Laurence? I was nineteen.' She dropped her gaze for a second. 'How long ago it all seems! Do you know when I came into the restaurant last night and saw you, it was strange, like seeing a ghost. I felt as if I were seeing myself. I felt so sorry for you . . .'

'*Sorry* for me?'

'Yes, Katharine.' The violet eyes fixed her once more. 'Tell me,' she said unexpectedly, 'do I look miserable? No, don't answer—I know I do. He's left the marks of our life together on my face, hasn't he? And you can't disguise that. Not if you paint an inch thick.' She laughed softly.

She was going to have to lie, Katy suddenly thought desperately. She had to get out of this somehow.

'Look,' she said quickly, 'I don't know why you've come here or what you want. Whatever happened in the past, it's nothing to do with me . . .'

'Oh, but it is, Katharine.' Camilla spoke gently but with complete certitude. 'You're not the first, you know. And you won't be the last. *That's* why I've come to see you. You see, I want you to know something—you have a right. You must understand Laurence, you must understand that . . . it's a compulsion with him. It's almost like the need for an audience. He has to have it, the sensation of conquest . . .'

'Please.' Katy felt she couldn't stand it any longer, this soft whispery voice, the veiled accusations. 'We shouldn't be having this conversation, it's wrong, it's . . .'

'Katharine,' Camilla leaned towards her, 'do you want me to tell you what happened last night, after you and he were alone together? I could, you know. He was angry, I expect, wasn't he? No, don't answer, I could write the whole scenario. He was violent, wasn't he? Just enough to break your resistance? He likes breaking people, Katharine, it excites him, haven't you noticed?'

Katy fought the memory, but it came back—that strange glittering look in Laurence's eyes, the threats, the scene over the dress. Her heart turned over and she began to feel sick. How could Camilla be so accurate? She stood up abruptly; this had to be stopped.

'I'm sorry,' she said stiffly, 'I don't want to listen to this, I should prefer it if you would go.'

Camilla didn't get up. Instead she took out a cigarette and lit it, inhaled, taking her time.

'All right,' she said finally, 'I will. I expected you to be this way. Laurence likes young girls, but he never selects easy quarries. I'll go, but not before I've said what I came to say.'

Katy hesitated, unsure what to do. Physically it was impossible to get rid of her. She would just have to stay and listen, she thought desperately. She'd just have to try and close her ears to everything this woman said . . .

'I love him, Katharine.' She said it flatly, but Katy felt a stab of pain go through her at the words. 'I may as well be truthful—I still love him, in a way. I met him when I was hardly out of school. I was Catholic, convent-educated, and I wouldn't sleep with him. That's why he married me. And then he broke me—it's quite a simple story really. He broke me with his lies and his womanising, just as he'll break you,

Katharine. And it wasn't just one or two affairs, believe me!'
She laughed bitterly. 'There were scores of women. My friends,
our maid, other actresses   he's a wonderful lover,
Katharine, though *you* don't know how wonderful yet, do
you? He never had any problems. He'd have them, and leave
them, and he always made sure I knew all about it .'

Katy stared at her in horror. Suddenly she felt faint, and she sat
down again, the blood rushing to her heart. What did Camilla
mean by that, how could she know   Could all this be true?

'It all came out at the divorce, of course.' Camilla shrugged.
'Or most of it. He didn't even trouble to deny it, he couldn't,
the evidence was all there. My father had hired a private de-
tective. It was very sordid.'

That was *true*, Katy thought, fear tightening every muscle
in her body. She'd read the reports; the divorce had been un-
contested, Laurence had brought no evidence.

'He thought I'd never go through with it, you see,
Katharine. But I did, and he's never forgiven me for it. That's
why he won't leave me alone, it's become an obsession with
him, do you see? I was the one woman who got away, and I
was his wife. He can't bear that. He's a Catholic too, remember . It's destroyed me, and it nearly destroyed him—
all the lies. That's why he won't risk the theatre any more,
why he makes those ridiculous films. He thinks lies don't show
up on celluloid.

'He wants me back, of course. If we remarried he thinks he
could work on the stage again, that all the lies would be wiped
out. But I've told him, I'd sooner be dead. Let me tell you . . .'

Her voice ran on and on. She was describing an incident
from their marriage, how Laurence had taken some girl back
to their house and she had found them together . . . Katy
hardly heard her any more. Suddenly it was all beginning to
make hideous sense to her—the savagery when he spoke of his
wife, his refusal ever to discuss his marriage, his behaviour
that time in the village church. Camilla *couldn't* be lying, she
thought, you couldn't make up such a story. She felt all the
tension and confusion of the past weeks burgeoning inside
her. Jane was right, she thought, she ought to go back to
England, to people she knew, to places she knew, just so that
she could *think*, so she could get away and try to understand.
And yet, and yet—last night . . .

Uncannily, as if she were a mind-reader, Camilla broke off her story and crossed over to her.

'Never mind all that,' she said softly. 'That's past. We must talk about now. About you, Katharine. He's asked you to marry him, hasn't he?'

'*What?*' Katy felt her blood go cold, and stared into Camilla's face in stupefaction. Camilla smiled gently, and took her hands.

'Don't deny it, Katharine, what's the point? I know because *he* told me. He's told me everything,' her soft voice rushed on, 'that's why he kept coming to see me in Cannes. I know everything—about his secretary, about how he tricked you, about that boy-friend of yours back in London. About keeping you to himself here, all these weeks, never touching you, so that when he finally made his move . . .' She laughed softly. 'I know everything, Katharine. He's been boasting about it all these weeks. He thought it would hurt me, you see, and when it didn't seem to be hurting enough—he loves to cause pain, Katharine—then he said he was going to marry you. It's his last revenge, Katharine. He wants to marry you to hurt *me* . . .'

'That can't be true!' Katy heard herself stammering. 'He wouldn't.'

'How else could I know?' Camilla smiled gently. 'Katharine, believe me, I know where you've been, what you've eaten, what you wore, what you said to him. How you went to Mass, to the beach with the children, how he pretended to get drunk. Why do you think he brought you to Cannes last night? That wasn't for your benefit, Katharine, it was for *mine*. He knew I'd be there, and he put on quite a performance . . .'

Then it was true. Suddenly Katy had no more doubts. Her heart felt as if it were breaking. All those times they had been together, when she had been so happy . . . he'd just been using her, she thought, in anger and pain. Everything that had happened, all the past month, it was smashed, hideously smashed.

She would have to get away, she thought. Somehow she must. She never wanted to see him again after such a betrayal. If *only* she could go back to London . . .

'Katharine, I know what you're thinking, and you're right.' Camilla knelt down beside her. 'That's why I came here today.

You must go away—and you could, don't you see that? Your friends are flying back this afternoon, aren't they? You could go with them, Dick and I will drive you into Cannes. Believe me, Katharine, it's easier that way. No scenes. And then, in London, you'll have time to think. We can meet, if you like, I can show you things, letters—horrible letters! Don't let him force you to stay here, Katharine, don't you see that's what he wants?'

'I could . . .' Katy could hardly speak, and she felt the tears spill down her face. 'Jane said . . .'

'Of course.' Camilla put her arms about her, and drew her gently to her feet. 'What have you to lose? Ask yourself, Katharine. It's the most important decision of your life; don't you think you ought to make it in peace, at home, with your friends? Don't make the mistake I made, Katharine. Don't let him destroy another life, I beg you.' She had drawn her towards the door.

'Listen,' she said softly, as if she were coaxing a child, 'their flight's at three, isn't it? Come now, and you can be with them at the Metropole in an hour. I'll help you pack . . .' She opened the door into the hall. 'You don't even need to show me the way.' She gave a rueful smile. 'I know which room you're in. His mother's, isn't it? He told me.'

That finished it. Katy gave her her hand, and like a sleep-walker, allowed herself to be led up to her room. Dick Hunt was hovering in the hall, she saw; there was no sign of coffee. In the bedroom, it was Camilla who did the packing, swiftly and efficiently. She found the black dress, felt the torn straps, held it up in front of her for a moment, and looked in the glass.

'My poor Katharine,' she said, and bundled it into the case.

She left the black lace scarf Laurence had given Katy thrown over the bed.

'Better leave it,' she said softly, as Katy turned back for it. 'He gave it to you, didn't he? I know, I have one just like it.'

The whole thing took no more than ten minutes. When they came back downstairs and put on their coats, Dick Hunt had already gone down to the car. He was there in the courtyard, with the engine running. Gaston was standing at the door of his house, Katy saw, with the three children peeping out behind him. At the sight of them, Katy's heart turned over, and she hesitated. Quickly Camilla tucked her into the back of the car like an invalid, then she went across to Gaston. Katy sat there like an automaton. Every nerve in her body felt numb with pain. Camilla was talking, gesturing . . .

'Don't you want to sit in the front, honey?' Dick Hunt grinned at her in the car mirror. 'You do give yourself airs, don't you? Lucky for me Camilla isn't so choosy, don't you think?'

Katy felt herself freeze. There was something wrong with all this, she thought suddenly. Were he and Camilla lovers? Was that what he meant? And why was everything so pat, the car all ready, the hurry . . .

'Wait a moment,' she said.

But Camilla got quickly into the front and he immediately accelerated away. Katy sank back on the seats. She was being stupid, she thought, overreacting. That was all he meant. He just meant Camilla didn't mind sitting next to him . . .

'Take the coast road, Dick,' Camilla said peremptorily. 'It's quicker.' She turned round and gave Katy a wide, somehow vacant smile. 'We don't want to miss your friends, Katy, do we?'

She turned back, and Katy stared at the back of her glossy head. Unease had taken possession of her. The coast road. She and Laurence had taken it once, driving to a beach. It was tiny, winding and narrow, with precipitate bends over sheer cliffs. And it *wasn't* quicker. The fast way to Cannes was the autoroute, she was sure of it. So why were they taking it? But of course, she thought. Laurence might be on his way back; he'd take the other road, the fast road—he always did. Why was Camilla so anxious to avoid him?

She tensed, looking out at the road ahead. Dick drove surprisingly well, but the route was slowing them down. The wind was buffeting the car so hard he was having difficulty holding it on the road. Rain lashed the windscreen in gusts; the wipers hardly coped. They had to stop to let a shepherd and a flock of goats cross the road, and Katy heard him swear softly.

Camilla seemed to be getting agitated too, Katy could sense it. She kept turning round as if to see if they were being followed. She fiddled with her gloves and her bag. She said nothing to Katy at all now—it was as if, once in the car, she had forgotten her presence. As they began the long twisting climb up to the coast, she looked at her Cartier watch.

'Hurry it up, Dick,' she said impatiently. 'We don't want to miss the flight.'

'For God's sake, Camilla,' he said irritably, 'what do you want me to do, fly? You can see what the road's like.'

'Just get us there,' she said, and her voice was suddenly different, icy cold and sharp, its pitch higher than usual.

Dick Hunt glanced across at her.

'Take a pill, Camilla,' he said sharply.

'I can't. I left the bloody things at the hotel . . .'

As if sensing Katy's disquiet, Dick grinned at her again in the mirror.

'Camilla's on Valium,' he said shortly. 'This whole thing's been getting to her, you know.'

Katy edged across the back seat so she was behind Dick Hunt and near the door. She could see Camilla better from there. Valium? She stared. Camilla had gone chalk white; her eyes were glazed; her hands were shaking. She tried to light a cigarette, but couldn't keep her lighter steady . . .

'*God!*' Camilla spat out the word. Dick Hunt slowed, and she finally managed to light the cigarette. She inhaled deeply.

In that moment Katy decided. There was something dreadfully wrong. She didn't like any of it. *Why* had she agreed to come? She must have been mad, she thought. She had always hated Dick Hunt; she didn't trust either of them . . . suddenly she didn't believe anything Camilla had told her.

'Please,' she said abruptly, 'Dick, will you stop the car? I don't want to go to Cannes. I want to go back. I . . .'

Dick Hunt slowed, and Camilla began to laugh.

It was a horrible laugh, and it went on and on, rising in pitch as if it would never stop. Katy stared at her in disbelief. It was like her dream, she thought suddenly, just like her dream . . .

'Not just now, honey,' Dick accelerated again, and swung the car round sharply on to the coast road. 'Camilla's not feeling well. Let's just get into Cannes, shall we?'

The car lurched round the bend, and for a sickening moment Katy saw the drop below them. The cliffs here were high, it was a hundred feet down on to jagged rocks. She felt her stomach turn over.

'Stop!' she heard herself cry. 'Please, Dick, stop the car. I'll walk back.'

'Oh, my God, she wants to *walk* back,' Camilla said, and the laugh started again, higher and higher.

'Shut up, Camilla!' Dick Hunt said violently. He swerved, narrowly missing a rock by the roadside. 'Calm down, can't you? We're at the top of the rise. It's downhill all the way from here, honey . . .'

As the car gathered pace, Katy knew what she must do. He wasn't going to stop, she knew it. And she had to get out of that car . . .

Quietly she edged across the seat to the door on the inside of the road. It wasn't locked. She peered through the rain at the road ahead, trying to remember it. Yes, she recognised where they were, she thought with relief, she had been this way. In a minute they would be coming to a hairpin bend— there was a turn-off there to the autoroute, and it was blind, he'd have to slow down, and then . . . She rested her fingers on the door handle, feeling suddenly totally calm. Yes, they were nearly there. Any moment . . .

When they were perhaps forty yards from the bend they suddenly heard the blast of a horn.

'Dick! There's something coming the other way!' Camilla cried. There was no time for him to change down, he slammed his foot on the brakes, and as the car started to slide on the wet road, the other car rounded the bend towards them at speed. It was a cream and black Lagonda . Katy had no time to think. She pressed the handle, and pushed her full weight against the door. As she did so, Camilla started to scream. She hit Dick Hunt's hands, reached across frenziedly and wrenched at the wheel. With a sickening screech of tyres they went into a skid, and the violent movement threw Katy against something hard. She felt rain on her face, then something tore at her arm, pain shot through her back like a knife, her head hit something and she felt as if she were floating. Blood came before her eyes like a dark veil; there was a smell of petrol, burning rubber, and then the hideous endless crash of metal hitting metal at high speed. She saw nothing but sky; a gull wheeling . . . But she heard it all with slow dreamlike clarity. *He's dead,* she thought. Then the dark blood washed over and she went under.

CHAPTER TEN

SHE was in a room. It was cool and dark, shadowy, she couldn't see properly. There was a constant whirring noise that seemed to come from above her, and cool air brushed her skin. Sometimes she thought she saw movement in the room, white shapes, whispering. Then it would stop and there was blackness again, a wonderful peaceful blackness, like velvet, so soft and so deep she could swim in it and it would be good, she felt, just to let go, to sink, to let it envelop her. She rested, poised, in the blackness, she wanted it to wrap her. A voice was speaking to her, a voice she knew, saying her name over and over again, calling her.

But she didn't want to come out of the blackness, it was so peaceful. The voice wouldn't go away, it was like a litany, over and over again, and she could smell something, not incense, but something sour and sharp that felt cold when it touched her. The cold made the blackness recede a little, and she shaped her lips to call it back. Then the voice began again, *Katharine, Katharine, Katharine . . .*

There was a shape, she could see it. The blackness had gone away. The shape moved, the whispering began again.

'De l'eau, vite, elle se réveille . . .'

Her mouth—it felt dry. Something cold and wet bathed her lips. There was a dark shape in the room now; it was beside her. She swam in cool grey water, but the shape was always there. It touched her, and she held on to it. She didn't want to sink any more, she wanted to hold on to that dark shape, it was like a rock, she needed it. If it weren't there, she would drown.

It was gone. She reached for it, she must find it . . . she opened her eyes. A woman in a long white veil was there, and bent over her. Katy tried to speak, but her lips were stiff, they wouldn't move. The woman smiled.

'Taisez-vous, ma petite, restez tranquille . . .'

The dark shape was there again. It wasn't a rock, she knew

172

that now. How stupid she was! Her mind seemed so slow, eddying back and forth. Of course it wasn't a rock, it was

'Laurence!' She had screamed the word; she was sitting bolt upright. She could see now. A white bed, cabinets, a fan in the ceiling, everywhere tubes and bandages. The woman was beside her.

'Where is he?'

'Sssh, *ma petite!*' The woman rested a cool hand on her forehead. *'Vous êtes malade, vous comprenez . . . restez tranquille . . .'*

'Where *is* he?'

There was a flurry of movement, doors opening and shutting. Someone took her arm and she felt a sharp pain. She wanted to sleep—oh, she wanted so to sleep.

She opened her eyes again. On the wall opposite was a statue of a woman in a blue dress holding a baby. There was a notice in gold letters: *Couvent du Sacré-Coeur*. The room was small, plain, spotlessly clean. By the door the woman in the white veil sat reading. Katy lay there, listening as the pages of the book were turned. There was a tube fixed to her arm, she could feel it now; lazily she turned her head and watched the colourless liquid drip from the bottle into the tube. Water, not blood, she thought distantly. And with that she remembered.

She sat up and her eyes met those of the woman by the door, who looked up, startled by her movement.

'He's dead, isn't he?' Katy spoke with perfect clarity.

The woman got up and came towards her. Without answering, she took Katy's wrist in a cool hand and felt her pulse.

Katy lay back on the pillows and turned her face away.

'Je vais chercher le docteur . . .'

She left the room, her skirts rustling, and the door swung shut quietly behind her. Katy lay looking up at the ceiling, watching the fan revolve and revolve. Her vision blurred with tears. Why hadn't she been killed too? She knew why the nun had left her; the doctor would break the news. Wasn't that how they did things?

She closed her eyes and felt the tears run hot over her cheeks. The door swung softly open. She could hear a whispered consultation going on in French. Perhaps they were discussing whether to tell her now, or later, she thought. It didn't matter. Nothing mattered now.

'Katharine.'

She didn't open her eyes. She didn't believe her ears. She had gone back into that limbo world between wake and dreaming . . .

'Katharine.'

He was there. She opened her eyes and she could see him, a dark figure beside her bed, looking down at her. How cruel dreams were!

He bent and took her hand, then raised it and pressed it to his lips. His cheeks were wet. She uncurled her fingers and let them trace the lines of his face—the dark brows, the lines from nose to mouth. His skin felt rough, he needed a shave . . . she smiled.

'Laurence?' If she spoke he would disappear again, she knew it. He didn't move, and she stared at his face. It looked different, haggard, as if he hadn't slept for days. There was a long thin scar that ran down the side of his face from his temple to cheekbone. That had never been there, her mind said lazily. And suddenly she became alert. She struggled to sit up, and his arms enfolded her.

'You're not going to go away? Laurence . . .' Feverishly she touched him, his skin, his thick hair. He didn't answer her. With a low groan he clasped her to him, crushing her against his chest, and her ears were filled with the drumming of his heart. They stayed like that for what seemed to her an eternity, then with great gentleness he released her and settled her back on the pillows.

'Don't let go of me!' she cried at once, reaching for his hand.

'Hush,' he said softly. 'You've been very ill, Kate. You mustn't get excited, it'll start the fever up again.'

She stared at him, her eyes brimming with tears. 'I thought you were dead,' she told him. 'Oh, Laurence, I was sure of it. I heard the crash, you see, and I saw your car, just before I jumped, I saw it . . .'

He rested his hand gently against her lips.

'Don't talk,' he said. 'Don't think about all that now. It's over. I'm here, I promise you. I never tell lies, remember?'

She stared at his dark shadowed face, and her heart turned over. She was to blame for all this. She had judged him a liar, she had believed Camilla and gone in the car. If she hadn't all this would never have happened . . .

'It's all my fault,' she cried desperately.

Laurence shook his head. 'Kate, don't,' he said gently. 'You're still not well. You were unconscious for three days. You mustn't think of all that now. You must get well, and strong again, and . . .'

'I have to know, Laurence,' she fought to calm herself, and spoke as deliberately as she could. 'I want you to tell me. I don't want to have to find out from some nurse, or a doctor. What happened?'

His eyes darkened, and he looked away.

'Camilla's dead, isn't she?'

'Yes,' he said softly. 'The car went over the cliff. There was nothing anyone could have done, Kate.'

'And Dick?'

'He was thrown clear. He's out of hospital already. I think he's gone back to London.'

'And you?'

'As you see.' He ran his fingers down the scar on his face.

'No more?' She stared at him anxiously.

He smiled gently. 'No more,' he said. 'For once the gods must have been with me.'

'Thank you for telling me.'

She stared into those dark eyes, and saw the pain behind the smile. He was trying to be gentle for her sake, she thought, and she turned her face away. *Je suis le veuf, le ténébreux, l'inconsolé:* the line from the poem swam back into her consciousness again: the widower, the dark one, the inconsolable . . . How horribly it had all come true, as if it had been willed. She closed her eyes. There could be, she knew, no forgiveness . . .

'Kate.' She opened her eyes. 'You must sleep now. Don't think about all this, I beg you. All that matters now is for you to get strong and well again. In a few days, if the doctors agree, you can come back to La Bayardière. I've hired an English nurse already. You'll be well looked after . . . would you like that?'

'I should go back to London,' she said weakly. 'You mustn't . . . not now.'

'I'll be the judge of that.' He smoothed her pillows. 'Now, go to sleep. I'll stay with you. I shan't leave you.'

'You'll be here in the morning?' She clutched at his hand.
He nodded grimly. 'Yes,' he said, 'I shall. This time.'

'Well now, and how are we feeling this morning?'

The English nurse was plump, with bright red hair, and she
was formidably hearty. Katy had been back at La Bayardière
for over a week now, and the nurse had unbent so far as to
admit that her name was Elizabeth. Only Laurence Martineau,
however, was sufficiently in favour to be allowed to use the
name; for Katy—as if to retain the formalities of their relationship—she remained Nurse Jones. She bustled around the
room now, her starched skirts swishing, opening the shutters,
turning back the covers. She surveyed her patient keenly.

'Well, we *do* look a little better, don't we? Some colour in
the cheeks at last. That little walk yesterday must have done
some good. Still, we mustn't be overdoing things, must we?
Another week at least before I'll be on the plane back to
London. Now . . .' She lifted Katy forward and plumped at the
pillows. 'We've a proper breakfast this morning, and we're
going to try and eat it, aren't we? None of that French rubbish,
those horrible croissant things and a bit of jam. I don't call
that a breakfast. We've got porridge today, and a boiled egg
and toast and tea . . .'

She produced a laden tray. Katy stared at it in amazement.
'*Porridge?* Wherever did you find that here?'

Nurse Jones gave a complacent smile and adjusted her cap.
'Where there's a will, there's a way, I've always said.' She
smiled. 'I had a word with Mr Martineau, and he went into
Cannes for it specially. There's nothing like porridge, I said,
for setting someone up in the morning.'

Katy tasted it; it was delicious. Suddenly she felt tremendously
hungry. She began eating voraciously, feeling as if she hadn't
touched food for weeks. Nurse Jones pottered about the room,
straightening things, which was her passion. She liked everything on a table to be laid out in straight lines—like surgical
instruments, Katy thought, watching her with a smile.

'Now,' she went on, 'I think we could have a proper bath
this morning, don't you?'

'Could we wash my hair?' Katy said pleadingly.

'Well now, don't let's try and run before we can walk. There
were a few stitches there at the back, but they've healed up

nicely. We'll have to see how we go.' The nurse turned for the
tray. 'There now,' she said happily, 'haven't we done well!
Not a scrap left. You're on the mend, young lady.'

Nurse Jones disappeared into the bathroom, and Katy heard
the welcome sound of bathwater running. A bath, she thought
longingly. How wonderful . . .

'What do you think you're doing?' Nurse Jones was back in
the room. 'We don't try and get out of bed yet—not on our
own, we don't.'

'Nonsense,' Katy said. 'I'm perfectly well, really I am,
Nurse. I feel much stronger.'

'That's as may be.' Nurse Jones gave her a keen glance.
'You've lost a lot of weight, and you're not used to being on
your feet yet. You behave, my girl, and do just what I tell you,
and there might be a surprise for you this morning.'

'A surprise?' Katy turned to her in excitement.

'If we behave. Now, into the bath with you.'

She relented about the hair, and let Katy wash it, just as she
had hoped. Then she wrapped her in a thick towelling dressing
gown and disappeared mysteriously next door to the bedroom.
When she returned, her cheeks were pink.

'Now,' she said, 'what do you think of this, then?'

She held out her arms. In them was the most exquisite
nightdress Katy had ever seen, of the finest white silk, heavy
with lace. Katy stared.

'With Mr Martineau's compliments. That was the message.
More or less,' Nurse Jones said drily.

'For me?'

'Well, it's certainly not for me, dear. Now, let's put it on,
and then back into bed. He'll be visiting as usual this morning.'

She helped Katy into it, then stood back, admiringly.

'What a picture!' she said warmly. 'That'll make Mr
Martineau very happy, that will. You look quite lovely, my
dear. Well on the road to recovery, I'd say. And that'll be a
weight off *his* mind, I can tell you.'

Katy looked away. The nightdress was so beautiful, but she
felt she had no right to wear it. And she wasn't looking forward to his visit. He came every morning, every afternoon, for
just the time Nurse Jones allowed. He was gentle and considerate and kind. Every time he looked at her, every time he

touched her, she felt tortured with guilt. She could see the pain in his eyes, however much he tried to hide it .

'Nurse,' she said quickly, 'how much longer do you think it will be before I'm well enough to go back to London?'

Nurse Jones avoided her eyes.

'No call to be talking about that yet,' she answered gruffly. 'Get well first and then think about it, I'd say. And you don't want to cause Mr Martineau any more worry, now do you?'

'Is he worried?' Katy allowed herself to be led docilely back into the bedroom, and settled in bed.

'Is he worried?' Nurse Jones stared at her. 'Why, bless me, you've got eyes in your head, haven't you? I look at him sometimes, and I think if we don't watch out I'm going to have two patients on my hands. Him hardly eating, and up half the night, pacing up and down. I said to him, I said, "Mr Martineau, when I make a breakfast for someone, I expect it to be eaten. And I expect a body to sleep nights, too." . . . Worried indeed!'

Katy said nothing. Maybe Laurence was concerned for her recovery, but it was not that that kept him awake at night, she was sure of it. She sank back on the pillows, feeling suddenly exhausted. She must get well, she thought tiredly. She must get back to London as soon as she could. She had no right to be here, not after all that had happened.

'Now, all settled, are we? Well, I'll be off, then.' Nurse Jones made a final adjustment to the bedcover, which was half an inch out of line. 'He'll be up in a while, I've no doubt. And I'll be seeing you later. I'm taking the morning off, as we're so much better today. That Marie-Christine's taking me shopping. No excitement, mind!' She paused at the door. 'We don't want a setback, do we? I'll see you later, my dear. Just you rest now. Mind,' she gave Katy an uncharacteristically wicked grin, 'if I had a lovely man like that coming to see me, I'd be more than a bit excited!'

She nipped out smartly, before Katy could reply, and Katy smiled to herself wanly. The lovely man! She had been so near to him, so close to happiness, and now it was all gone. She had failed him, when he had asked her to trust him. It had all been so simple—and now . . .

'You're feeling better, I hear.'

Laurence was standing in the doorway, and had come in so quietly that she hadn't even heard him. She started.

He crossed swiftly to the bed and stood looking down at her, at her face, her bare throat, the line of silk and lace that lay over the swell of her breasts. She felt herself colouring; that look brought back such bitter-sweet memories . . .

'You don't need to answer. I can see for myself.' He took her hand, and pressed it lightly to his lips, and a tremor went through her.

She felt that terrible weakening in her limbs that his closeness always aroused in her, and to her horror and shame, something else, a quickening, the flutterings of desire. She looked away. She must put all those feelings from her.

'You like the nightdress?'

'Oh, yes! It's beautiful. You're so kind, you shouldn't have . . .'

'You look like a bride,' he said slowly, his eyes burning into hers. 'On her wedding night.'

Katy felt a stab of pain go through her like a knife. What might have been. What she had destroyed.

'Kate.' She heard the thickening in his voice, and she could see the hunger in his eyes. Before she could protest, or ward him off, he gathered her gently to him, and pressed his lips upon hers. 'Kate,' he murmured, 'Kate. All these weeks!' She felt her body go pliant in his arms, and a sweetness flowed through her veins which it was impossible to fight off. Her lips parted under his, his hands stroked her skin and her hair, and she could feel it rising within her, all the desire she felt for him . . . she curved her head back, so he could kiss her throat, and heard his breath catch.

'No, Laurence—no!' From somewhere within her she found the strength. She put her hand up and stopped his kisses. Instantly he drew back.

'I'm sorry,' he said stiffly, 'I was forgetting. You're not well yet. I shouldn't have . . .'

'No, it's not that . . .' She couldn't meet his gaze, and she felt as if the conflict of feelings within her would drive her mad, but she knew she had to speak now. She mustn't leave it any longer. 'Laurence . . .' She forced herself to speak. 'I . . . I want to go back to London. This isn't right. And if I stay here, I know I'll . . .'

She broke off. Laurence sat down on the bed and looked at her grimly.

'You're not going back,' he said flatly. 'Not without me, anyway.'

'No, but I must . . .'

'You were going back before,' he said. 'You changed you mind then. You tried to jump out of the car. How many more times are you going to change it?'

He looked at her so sternly that Katy felt she would faint. She couldn't bear it any more, she thought, she couldn't stand it if it all ended in more pain.

'Please, Laurence,' she begged. 'We don't need to talk about it, do we? We both understand what's happened. It's better to end it without argument . . .'

'I have no intention of arguing with you.' He folded his arms and looked at her coldly. 'If you really want to go back to London, if you mean it, then I suppose you'll have to go. When you're well again. Not before. And not before I've had the chance to explain things to you.'

She sighed. 'There's nothing to explain,' she said dully.

'There's everything to explain!' She could hear the sudden anger in his voice and she flinched. 'Damn you, Katharine! Do you think I'm going to let you off the hook, just because you've been ill, because you can't wait to run away? Well, I'm damn well not going to. You can sit there and you can listen for once, and while you're about it you can explain some things to me as well. God! I've been on the rack all these weeks, and now you think you're just going to waltz off. Well, you're not, Katharine, and you'd better realise it!'

'That's not true!' She stared at him angrily, two points of bright colour coming into her cheeks. 'I'm not running away . . .'

'You ran away before!'

'That was because Camilla . . .' She broke off, horrified. Whatever had happened, whatever Camilla had done, she couldn't talk about it now.

'Yes?'

'I . . . I don't want to talk about it.'

'You'll damned well have to talk about it!' He gripped her hand so hard that he hurt, and his eyes blazed back into hers. Katy was silent, and neither of them moved for a moment.

Laurence's breath was coming quickly. Finally he let go of her hand.

'All right,' he said slowly, 'then tell me something else. In the car, before you jumped, what happened then? Why did you do it?'

She stared at him, and hesitated.

'Well,' she said finally, reluctantly, 'I just felt that something was wrong, that . . . that I was doing the wrong thing. They took the coast road, and I thought that was odd, because they said it was the quickest way, and I knew it wasn't . . .'

He nodded and she drew breath.

'And then she—Camilla—she started behaving oddly. She became very agitated, her voice was different . . .' She paused. Since then, she had hardly dared to think of it, but now the scene came back with a sickening clarity. 'I . . . I asked them to stop, and let me out, and they wouldn't. They just went faster and faster. Then, when we were coming up to the bend . . .' She faltered, and Laurence took her hand. 'They heard your horn. I already had my fingers on the door-handle. I don't know—it all happened so quickly. I saw your car. Camilla saw it too, and she was screaming, and she caught hold of the wheel . . .'

She turned her face away, the tears welling from her eyes. He leant towards her.

'Katharine, listen, it's important. Did Camilla take anything in the car?'

'Take anything?' She stared at him blankly. Then the memory came back. 'Yes,' she said quickly. 'Yes! She did. Or rather, Dick told her to take a pill, and she said she'd left them at the hotel. That's right! I remember now, he said she was on Valium . . .'

'Valium!' He snorted. 'Didn't you realise then?'

'Realise?' She hesitated. 'She did look very ill. Her hands were shaking, I remember . . .'

He sighed.

'Katharine, don't you understand? Camilla was an *addict*. She had been for years. I thought something like that must have happened.'

She stared at him. 'An addict? Camilla? You mean heroin?'

He shook his head, and she saw all the old pain and darkness flood into his eyes.

'Katharine,' he said, 'I know it's painful, but will you let me explain? Will you let me tell you all the things I should have told you before?'

She nodded dumbly. He took her hand again, and began in a low voice, keeping his eyes on her.

'Camilla didn't take heroin,' he said. 'It wasn't that simple. She took a whole mixture of drugs—pills to wake up, pills to get through the day, pills to sleep at night. Amphetamines and barbiturates—uppers and downers. It was killing her. It had been for years. She's been in and out of clinics all over the world. She'd just been in another I'd found, in Switzerland. Dick Hunt discharged her.'

Katy stared at him, her eyes wide.

'She was an addict when I married her,' he said slowly. 'If she hadn't been, it wouldn't have happened. I didn't love her, you see.'

'You didn't love her?' She gazed at him in startled disbelief.

'I couldn't.' He gripped her hand. 'Dear God, I tried. I was younger then, I didn't understand that you can't will love into existence. It comes.' He looked at her intently. 'It comes of its own accord.'

'Then why did you marry her?' she said, her voice hardly above a whisper.

'For a lot of reasons. Stupid pride, mostly. She told me, you see, that I could save her, that I could get her off the drugs and nobody else could. That without me she was finished. And I believed her. I thought I might as well try and do one worth-while thing in my life. There had been women, but no one that mattered truly, ever. And so . . .' He shrugged. 'Well, I was wrong. I couldn't get her off the drugs. And she never forgave me for not loving her. Though she had so many lovers you might have thought it wouldn't matter.'

'*She* had lovers?' Katy stared at him, and Camilla's insidious voice snaked its way back into her brain.

'Many of them. You couldn't blame her. Our marriage was a purely formal one, almost from the first. Even a man—especially a man—can't simulate passion he doesn't feel.'

'But the divorce.' Katy gazed into his eyes. 'You never even brought evidence . . .'

'No,' he said coldly, 'I didn't. I gave Camilla the evidence she wanted, and the rest she invented. It wasn't hard. She had friends like Dick Hunt who were happy to perjure themselves, and at that point she thought she wanted to remarry, so she wanted it all over quickly. We'd been living separate lives for four years then, more or less. It seemed the best thing to do.'

'But how *could* you have? All those terrible stories, the lies— how could you bear it?'

'Katharine,' he took her hand, and held it to his heart, 'you must understand. I didn't care about all that. I didn't care one shred. I didn't hate Camilla—I couldn't, I felt too sorry for her, and she couldn't altogether help what she had become. But all I could see was the freedom, freedom from lies at last, freedom to begin my life again, except, of course, I wasn't entirely free. There was my religion. The Church didn't recognise our divorce, of course. And then—there was Camilla.'

'She said to me . . .' Katy hesitated. 'She said she still loved you.'

'Yes,' Laurence said quietly, 'I think that was true, in some mad twisted way it was true. She didn't remarry after all, you see. It fell through. And we were still in touch, over alimony, over clinics . . . it went on and on. When it came to it, you see, Camilla couldn't let go.'

She stared at him silently, her mind juggling the events of the past, and suddenly it did all begin to make sense. She remembered that sense of being hypnotised, taken over, when Camilla had talked to her, that extraordinary sensation of a huge, destructive will encased in a frail body.

'And then,' Laurence smiled wryly, 'then I met you. It's ironic, isn't it, that if it hadn't been for Camilla, I shouldn't have done so?'

'For Camilla?'

He nodded. 'You see, she'd known Hunt for years, since before even I met her. They had a strange relationship, one I never understood anyway. I think it was Hunt who first got her on to drugs. Anyway, he was the one person who could control her, dominate her. But he wanted her under his thumb—that's why he was so furious when she married me— he hated me from that moment, I think. Well,' he sighed, 'Hunt had persuaded her to appear on his programme, to make a full confession about the drugs. The idea, I think, was that she'd pretend she'd kicked it, but she'd talk about it at length—"Famous actress reveals secrets of drug dependence"

. . .' He laughed bitterly. 'You can imagine the sort of thing.'

Katy nodded silently. She could, only too well. It was the sort of thing Dick Hunt thrived on.

'I knew if she did it, she'd be finished as an actress. No one would hire her—I could foresee it. And I thought it quite likely she'd break down on the show, that it'd be clear she *hadn't* kicked the drugs. So I tried to stop it. And Hunt made one of his charming little bargains. He agreed to drop the show, if I agreed to appear in her place. So——' he shrugged, 'I don't even know now, if it was all true, if he really intended to do the programme with Camilla at all. But I couldn't take the risk. So I agreed. And I met you . . .'

'I see.' Katy bit her lip. What a strange man he was, she thought, so good, so generous, so protective—even to Camilla. 'I couldn't understand,' she said haltingly. 'When they told me about the programme, I thought then how strange it was that you should agree. Oh yes!' Suddenly she remembered something else. 'Of course. When I went through the cuttings for Dick Hunt, there was a picture of him and Camilla together— I thought it was him, but I couldn't be sure. I see now. That's why he sent me to check all the cuttings. He wanted to make sure there was nothing on record that could link him with Camilla—he must have taken that picture out . . .'

Laurence smiled grimly. 'Oh, it all went according to plan,' he said. 'There was just one factor that no one could predict. You, Katharine.'

'Me?' she said softly.

He drew her closer towards him.

'Katharine,' he said slowly, 'surely you understand? Why do you think Camilla came here to Cannes?'

She dropped her eyes. There was still that, she thought, and she felt a pang of dread shoot through her.

'She came here because of *you*, Katharine. That's why she left the clinic in Switzerland. Dick Hunt knew you were here— he must have found out somehow . . .'

'Oh, easily—from Lindy, his researcher. I told her.'

He nodded. 'Well, there you are. He went straight to Switzerland and told Camilla. They took the next plane to Cannes.'

'But *why*?' Katy stared at him with wide eyes. 'Why? I don't understand.'

'Well,' he smiled, 'I wouldn't pretend to have been celibate for the last ten years of my life. But I'd never brought any women here, ever. Perhaps it occurred to them that something a little unusual had happened.'

'But I know why you brought me here, you told me . . .' She turned away.

'Kate,' his voice broke, 'I didn't. I didn't explain—not properly. This whole hideous mess is my fault, don't you see that? I left you that morning, fool that I was, and I hadn't . . .' He stopped and looked away, and Katy held her breath. She felt as if her nerves were stretched to snapping point .

'Kate,' Laurence drew a deep breath, 'don't you understand?' He looked at her desperately. 'Do you remember,' he said haltingly, 'the day we first met, in that room at the airport?'

She nodded dumbly.

'When you came in looking furiously angry, and trying desperately to disguise it, to be polite to this actor you had to escort back to the studios? Well, I loved you then. I fell in love with you then, do you hear me? I loved you in that stupid Daimler, when you snapped at me, when I was rude, and you were rude straight back at me. I loved you in that damned lift, in the studios, when I could see only your face out of all the others in the audience, when you refused to have dinner with me.

'I loved you in that god-awful restaurant, with those god-awful phoney people, when you didn't give an inch, didn't try to be conciliatory, or polite, or charming. Why do you think I hit Hunt, you little fool? It wasn't just that he was insulting you. I couldn't stand to see another man's hands on you, not for a second, can't you understand that? You were mine, and I wanted him to know it. And then . . .'

He broke off. 'Kate,' he said, his voice low and painful. 'Don't you understand? I've loved you from the first instant I saw you—as I've never loved anyone in my life. I knew I had to have you, had to have you with me. I asked you to come here for a few months, because I thought I had no right to ask for more, because I thought you cared for someone else. But as soon as you came here I knew it wasn't enough. My darling love, I wanted you for always . . .'

Katy felt as if her heart would burst, and a great wave of

joy and love for him rose up inside her. Suddenly she saw their way clear before them. The future was theirs; what did she care for the past?

He hesitated, and took her hand. 'You do believe me, don't you, Kate? Say you do, my darling. Nothing else in the world matters to me now . . .'

'Oh, Laurence!' she took his hand and held it against her flushed cheeks, which were wet with tears. 'I never thought, I never dreamed . . .'

He smiled, gently mocking her. 'Well, you're a very blind as well as a very wilful young woman. But I expect you'll learn.'

'I'm not so blind!' she protested indignantly. 'You never gave me any sign, any indication, not for weeks. I thought about you every moment of the day, and dreamed of you each night, and you . . .'

'Oh, I don't know,' he said drily. 'I thought I gave the odd indication . . . Anyway, I may have deceived you, my darling, but I didn't deceive Camilla. That was my fatal mistake.'

'I don't understand . . .' She broke off. She didn't want to remember that scene with Camilla in the study, the things she had said. She didn't want even to think of it.

'My darling, I told her.' Laurence spoke calmly now, looking straight into her eyes. 'She arrived here in Cannes. She rang that very first morning, don't you remember? When you were sitting there typing, with your back to me, and I was wondering how long I could stand it before I went across and kissed you, and damn the consequences . . .

'I went to see her, and straight away there was trouble. She wanted to know why you were here, what had happened to my secretary—everything. There was a terrible scene, the worst I remember. So I told her the truth. I told her I'd met the only woman I should ever love. I told her I wanted to marry you. I thought she'd understand, after all this time. And she did seem to accept it. Suddenly she changed tack; she was reasonable about the whole thing, kind even. Then she kept making excuses to see me, and every time I went she'd ask me where we'd been, what we'd been doing. I told her then that I'd decided to do nothing, to say nothing. I thought you loved someone else, and it was nearly killing me. Then, when I found out I'd been wrong, that perhaps you might . . .

'I told her I was going to ask you to marry me. I thought

I'd better prepare her, because I expected trouble, but she seemed delighted. It was she who said I ought to bring you into Cannes, that if I did we all might meet. And so, when you said you wanted to go there, I thought—why not? I wanted you to see the past, Kate, do you see—my past. So that you could judge for yourself.'

She stared at him in silence, marvelling at Camilla's duplicity. And suddenly she felt a wave of pity for her. What she had said had been true, Katy thought, she must have been consumed with jealousy to have acted as she did . . .

'But that morning, the morning of the . . . accident,' she said gently. 'Why did you leave me then, Laurence?'

Pain rent his features. 'My God, Kate,' he said softly. 'After all that had happened, when you were in the hospital, and I was there by your bed, day and night, and I thought you might die . . . Kate, I could have killed myself then for having done it, for being such a damned fool. But I didn't think. I just knew suddenly that Camilla was up to something. I'd seen it at the Carlton, when she sent your friends home with us. I'd spent all the night thinking of it, and I only had one thought left by the morning. Whatever it was she was planning, I had to stop it. The thought of losing you, Kate of something going wrong . . . I couldn't stand it. So I drove straight into Cannes. She must have guessed what I'd do, because she left a chain of messages. I was sent from pillar to post—and then, suddenly, I realised. I got in the car, I had a premonition, and I took the coast road. You see, I knew that if she had been here, had tried to see you, she'd go back that way. She always took the coast road. But until I saw you there, all crumpled up by the roadside—oh, Kate, what had she *said* to you?'

Katy leaned across and took his face in her hands, very gently.

'Laurence,' she said, 'nothing that matters, and nothing that was true, and nothing I shall ever think of again, I promise you.'

'But you still want to go back to London?' His eyes searched her face, and she dropped her gaze.

'I thought——' she said hesitantly, 'I thought that now, perhaps, after what I did, you might want me to go.'

'No.'

'What do you want?'

He opened his mouth impetuously to speak, then his face changed. His eyes were clear, happier than she had ever seen them, she thought.

'Well,' he said in a matter-of-fact voice, 'I had certain things in mind . . .'

'Such as?' she said teasingly.

'You really want to know?' He leaned across and whispered into her ear for a few seconds, his hands stroking her neck and her hair, his lips close to her own. His words made the blood rush to her cheeks.

'That's just to begin with, of course,' he said drily, drawing back. 'There are other things, too.'

'As well as all that?' Katy said mockingly. Laurence smiled.

'Yes.' He looked down at her hands, and kept his voice flat, rather as if they were discussing a business agenda. 'I thought you might marry me. As soon as possible—today might be a good idea, but I don't want you going down the aisle supported by me on one side, and Nurse Jones on the other, so perhaps I might be prepared to wait . . . a few days. I thought you might marry me in the church here, in the village, and that Father Bernard might marry us—which would give an old man a great deal of pleasure. And I thought I might buy you a white lace veil to keep company with your black one. And I thought we might have a wedding breakfast—of lobster, to make up for the ones you cooked, when I was so churlish . . .'

He paused. 'Oh, and a few other things. That I might love you for the rest of my life, that you might come to my first nights when I go back to work in the theatre . . . That you might bear my children, and be as sweet a mother to them as you would be a wife to me, and that we might spend our wedding night in this room, with Provençal oak-leaves to bless us. That we might be, the two of us, quite content . . . Just a few things, you understand, but a long while to achieve them.'

He broke off, and looked down into her face, and she felt once more desire and a sweet happiness flood through her veins.

'Of course, it does rather depend on your answer,' he ended drily.

'Am I allowed to answer this time?' She smiled. 'Last time you wouldn't let me.'

'You are.'

'Then the answer is as it would have been then. Yes,' she said softly.

'As simply as that?' He looked at her wonderingly.

'As simply as that.'

'In spite of the past?' She saw still the pain of doubt in his eyes, and she held his gaze steadily.

'Because of the future,' she said gently.

'Kate! My heart's darling.' Swiftly he bent and gathered her into his arms, his lips searching for hers. She trembled at their touch, and as their mouths met Laurence gave a low groan of desire. The kiss bruised her lips with a sweet honeyed pleasure, and she felt desire for him burn in her body.

'Dear God, Kate,' he muttered, his hands seeking hers, and holding her at arm's length so he could look at her, 'you look so young and so frail and so . . . beautiful. And yet when you kiss me . . . where did you learn to kiss away a man's very soul?'

'From you,' she said softly. 'There has never been anyone else.'

'Nor shall there be, my darling.' He smiled, and she saw him fight to control the naked hunger for her in his eyes. 'I want you—I shall be fiercely jealous, can you bear that?'

'If I gave you cause, you mean?' she looked at him wickedly, lowering her lashes.

'You'd better not *glance* at another man, Kate—that would be cause enough . . .' He broke off. 'Of course, you know I'd never have let you leave here? Not if you'd begged and pleaded . . .'

'You wouldn't?'

'Certainly not. I'd have . . .' he hesitated, 'I'd have . . . kept you locked in the tower, with Nurse Jones as your guardian!'

Laughter tugged at the corners of his mouth and he tried to make his face grim and stern. Katy laughed with him.

'Nurse Jones?'

'Certainly. She's a pillar of strength. She's been a great comfort to me these past days when a certain young woman has been cool and distant, and I was going through hell. In fact,' he dropped his voice to a mock conspiratorial whisper, 'you know what she said to me?'

She shook her head.

'She said, "Mr Martineau, it may not be my place, but it's as plain as the nose on your face what's wrong here. You're pining for her, down here, and she's pining for you up there. You'd make my work a whole lot easier if you went up and sorted it out between you . . ." '

He gave an excellent imitation of Nurse Jones's somewhat gruff voice, and Katy dissolved in giggles.

'I don't believe she said any such thing!' she said. 'You've just made that up, Haven't you?'

Laurence smiled gently. 'Maybe.'

'Well, she said to *me* that I mustn't have any excitement,' Katy said mockingly.

'Did she now?' He leaned towards her, his dark eyes looking into hers, and gently, very deliberately, as if daring her to stop him, he undid, one by one, the white ribbons that laced the neck of her nightdress.

'You think that's a good prescription, Kate? No excitement?' He slid his hands gently under the lace, and at the touch of them against her bare skin, she caught her breath.

'I . . . I'm not sure . . .' she said, her lips curing into a long, slow smile, and she reached up and drew him closer to her. 'I think perhaps, just a little . . .'

'I think so too.' Laurence bent his head and kissed her and she felt again that languorous yet urgent pleasure begin to pulse in her body.

'I believe you planned all this,' she said lazily, sinking into his embrace. 'The nightdress and . . .' The words died away, she tried to challenge him with her gaze, but she wanted to close her eyes, to abandon herself to feeling, to touching.

'My darling Kate,' he held her strongly and surely, his lips warm against hers, 'I've planned so many things for us, but just now, for the moment, I should like to kiss my . . . wife. I think that would be a good thing, don't you? For our beginning?'

Give
Romance
this Christmas

The Mills & Boon Christmas Gift Pack is
available from October 8th in the U.K. It contains
four new Mills & Boon paperback Romances, in
an attractive presentation case:

Perfect Partner   – Carole Mortimer
Diamond Stud   – Margaret Mayo
A Temporary Affair – Kay Clifford
This Side of Heaven – Alexandra Scott

You do not pay any extra for the pack – so put it
on your Christmas shopping list now.
On sale where you buy paperbacks, £3.40 (U.K. net).

Mills & Boon
the rose of romance

How to join in a whole new world of romance

It's very easy to subscribe to the Mills & Boon Reader Service. As a regular reader, you can enjoy a whole range of special benefits. Bargain offers. Big cash savings. Your own free Reader Service newsletter, packed with knitting patterns, recipes, competitions, and exclusive book offers.

We send you the very latest titles each month, postage and packing free – no hidden extra charges. There's absolutely no commitment – you receive books for only as long as you want.

We'll send you details. Simply send the coupon – or drop us a line for details about the Mills & Boon Reader Service Subscription Scheme.
Post to: Mills & Boon Reader Service, P.O. Box 236, Thornton Road, Croydon, Surrey CR9 3RU, England.
*Please note: READERS IN SOUTH AFRICA please write to: Mills & Boon Reader Service of Southern Africa, Private Bag X3010, Randburg 2125, S. Africa.

Please send me details of the Mills & Boon Subscription Scheme.
NAME (Mrs/Miss) _____ EP3
ADDRESS _____
_____
COUNTY/COUNTRY_____ POST/ZIP CODE _____
BLOCK LETTERS, PLEASE

Mills & Boon
the rose of romance